Functional Skills HANDBOOK for MATHEMATICS Level 1

Author's Profile: Deborah Sanger

Deborah Sanger has a degree in Engineering, a PGCE (PCET) and an Adult Numeracy Specialist Tutor certificate.

She has worked in Further Education colleges for a number of years specialising in Adult Numeracy covering adult community classes, apprenticeship students and many other students within the college studying Key Skills, Basic Skills or Functional Skills Maths.

More recently, Deborah has specialised in working with awarding bodies in marking and assessing students' examination work and in writing and reviewing examination assessments.

She has also written student support materials for both Engineering and Functional Skills Maths.

Introduction

This handbook has been written to help you understand all the different topics in maths that you will need to know to pass a Functional Skills test at Level 1.

Each topic has been organised under its own heading so that you can easily find the pages you need to help you with anything you are not yet sure about, with suggestions for practice examples from everyday life.

Important facts, things to remember and areas where special care should be taken are highlighted throughout this book.

Each section begins with a section entitled **'Why do I need to know this?'**

The idea here is that you can see how this topic relates to everyday life.

One of the first questions people usually ask is 'Why do I need to learn about maths when I don't use it?' It is a good question, and there are two answers.

We all use maths every day without even realising it. Some examples are coming up.

Lots of research has been done to show how important maths can be for us.

When we use maths more confidently it can
- help to make us more successful at work
- give us longer and healthier lives
- give our children a better start in life too.

How do we use maths in everyday life?

For measuring things:
- Weighing out the ingredients in a recipe
- Measuring a room to work out how much paint or paper you need to decorate it
- Checking the size of something to see if it will fit into the space available

For comparing things:
- Checking special offers in the shops to find out if they are really as special as they sound and saving money on your shopping every week
- Finding out which of two things is the biggest
- Comparing weekly and monthly travel tickets to find the cheapest one
- Working out which place is the furthest away

For working things out:
- To make sure you have the right change for the bus
- To make sure you have enough money to buy fuel for your car
- To work out what time you need to do something
- Doubling or halving a recipe so that you have enough food and don't waste any
- Finding out just how much 25% off a sale item will save you
- Using a calculator

Functional Skills **MATHEMATICS**

For finding out useful information:
- Reading a bus timetable
- Using a calendar or diary
- Checking a price list
- Drawing and understanding a room plan

And very many more things too.

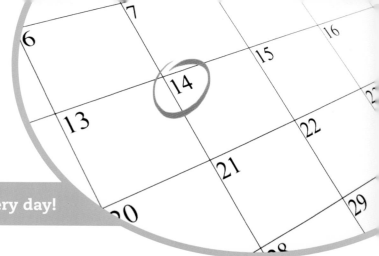

➡ **You can see how we all use maths every day!**

Why do we use numbers?

Lots of people think maths is confusing because of all the numbers. We all understand about how to read words in a book but a page of numbers can seem very confusing at first. Some maths even uses letters and symbols as well.

So, why do we use numbers?

The answer is because maths is really a bit lazy.
It is a short-hand way of writing everything out in full using words.

Look at this sum:

> Three plus two equals five

This takes a long time to write and it is very hard to see quickly what numbers we used in the sum or what number we got for the answer.

By using squiggly symbols we call numbers, instead of words, we can make it much easier for ourselves.

Using numbers it looks like this:

> $3 + 2 = 5$

It is very short and easy to read, we can easily pick out the number values, 3 and 2, and the answer, 5.

So all the numbers, little letters and symbols used in maths are just a shorthand way of writing out information to make it easier for ourselves.

Maths is lazy!

Functional Skills assessments and checking work

Why do I need to know this?
Functional Skills assessments are a bit different to most exams and tests.
There are things you need to know to help you to be successful in your test.

This book covers all the skills you need for Functional Skills, but what are Functional Skills?

Functional Skills assessments are designed to test your knowledge and skills in practical ways not just as a question and answer examination would.

During the course of this book you will learn a maths skill and then practise it so that you become more confident.

You will be able to use your new skills to help you solve new problems in different situations.

Functional Skills assessments will involve reading a question and then deciding for yourself how to answer it.

There are often different ways of getting the right answer so don't worry if you think your method is 'wrong'.
Your working out will show that you understood the question and you will get the marks for your answer.

How do you show that you understand what you were doing?

Functional Skills assessments give marks in different ways:
- for the way you work things out; this is called the *method*
- for *understanding* what you needed to do
- for *checking* your answer
- for *explaining* something you have done

Remember!
It is very important that you write down everything you do as you work something out. Don't miss any stages out.

This lets the examiner see what you were doing so they can work out if you understood how to use your maths skills to solve the problem.

Remember! →
It is very important that you check your answer.

There are often marks for showing you have checked your work. There are different ways of checking these which are shown later in this book.

Remember!
It is very important to read the question carefully and write any explanations or reasons you are asked for.

Functional Skills assessments often ask you to explain or give a reason why you have chosen something in your answer and marks are given for this. It is usually quite a simple explanation; you won't usually be expected to write more than a few words.

Reading, sorting and comparing numbers

Numbers can be very short or very long. Therefore we need a way of organising them so that we can use them to work things out.

➡ Numbers and place value

We use columns to help us keep the numbers tidy, then we can add, subtract and multiply without making any mistakes. We call this Place Value.

Look at these numbers

123,765	97,843	27	599

Numbers from 0 to 9 are called units. They go in the first column (U, short for units).

The UNITS are

123,76<u>5</u>	97,84<u>3</u>	2<u>7</u>	59<u>9</u>

T	U
	1
	2
	3
	4
	5
	6
	7
	8
	9
1	0

When we reach 9, we can't get any more numbers into the units column, so we start a new column called tens (T for tens). We can put a 1 in this column every time we get to ten.

In the number 10 the 1 tells us we have one ten and the 0 tells us we don't have any units.

Remember maths is lazy. If we just kept putting everything into the same column we'd get into a mess, so every time we get ten of something we just put a 1 in the new column.

Look at this pile of 13 coins. Lots of coins in one pile makes it difficult to count.

By putting them into piles of 10 we can easily see how many tens there are and how many are left over for the units column.

Here we have 1 ten and 3 units.

T	U
1	3

➡ Try this yourself with coins or counters

We can never put more than 9 into a column, so each time we reach 9 a new column has to be started on the left side. Each column is always ten times the value of the one on its right.

	M	HTh	TTh	Th	H	T	U		M	HTh	TTh	Th	H	T	U
Units from							0	to							9
Tens from						1	0	to						9	0
Hundreds from					1	0	0	to					9	0	0
Thousands from				1	0	0	0	to				9	0	0	0
Ten Thousands from			1	0	0	0	0	to			9	0	0	0	0
Hundred Thousands from		1	0	0	0	0	0	to		9	0	0	0	0	0
Millions from	1	0	0	0	0	0	0	to	9	0	0	0	0	0	0

So you can see how important it is to write numbers down carefully and keep the columns lined up and tidy.

Remember! →

A comma is put in after every thousand, that's every three place values, to make it easier to read larger numbers more quickly.

Take Care!
Every column has a special value and needs to be kept in line so we can add up and work with the numbers accurately.

Maths is tidy!

Sorting numbers by size

Now you know how to write numbers into their place value columns, you can sort numbers by size.

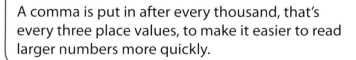

8	21,876,003		21,009	243
21	1,289	4,002	357	1,030
99	909,090		5,087,663	874

These can be written into size order using place value columns. Notice how the place values are all in neat lines or columns.

TM	M	HTh	TTh	Th	H	T	U
							8
						2	1
						9	9
					2	4	3
					3	5	7
					8	7	4
				1,	0	3	0
				1,	2	8	9
				4,	0	0	2
			2	1,	0	0	9
		9	0	9,	0	9	0
	5,	0	8	7,	6	6	3
2	1,	8	7	6,	0	0	3

U = Units
T = Tens
H = Hundreds
Th = Thousands
TTh = Ten Thousands
HTh = Hundred Thousands
M = Millions
TM = Ten Millions

You can order decimal numbers too and this is explained in the Decimals section of this book.

Functional Skills **MATHEMATICS**

Greater than and less than symbols

Sometimes when we sort numbers we want to compare them with each other.

Why do I need to know this?
These symbols are sometimes used in information you might read.
They are on a computer keyboard.
They are a useful abbreviation.

Instead of having to write:

| 23 is smaller than 457 | or | 21,000 is larger than 4,087 |

We can use Greater than (>) or Less than (<) symbols. Remember maths is lazy!

Greater Than

Equals

Less Than

Greater than and less than

| 23 < 457 | | 21,000 > 4,087 |

'Greater than' is another way of saying 'bigger than' or 'more than'.
'Less than' is another way of saying 'smaller than'.

Equals

| 8 = 8 |

When the number is the same, the lines don't meet at either end; that gives us the equals sign.
Think of the equals sign: the lines are both straight; they are parallel to each other.

Checking

You can easily check you have the symbol the right way round.
In the greater than and less than symbols one end of the equals sign has had the two lines closed together.

The closed end is next to the smaller number and the open end is next to the larger number.

Remember! →

<   the closed end is less than the open end   Less Than
>   the open end is greater than the closed end   Greater Than

Adding

There are different ways of adding numbers together. It doesn't matter which way you use as long as you are confident using it.

There are different words for adding, here are just some of them:

addition   plus   together

more than   make   count on

greater   double   sum

Why do I need to know this?

We add up every day, on the bus, shopping, buying things in shops, counting things up, working out which bus to catch and in many more activities.
There are different ways of working things out and getting the right answer.

➡ **Number lines**

This is an easy way of adding, or subtracting, smaller numbers. It would become more complicated with large numbers.

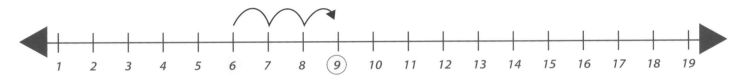

| 1 | 2 | 3 | 4 | 5 | 6 | 7 | 8 | 9 | 10 | 11 | 12 | 13 | 14 | 15 | 16 | 17 | 18 | 19 |

To add 6 and 3, find 6 on the number line and count 3 more places along. The answer is 9.

$$6 + 3 = 9$$

➡ **Number squares**

For larger numbers you can use a number square. The rows are ten numbers long so it is easy to count up in tens by moving down to the number below. Try:

65 + 34

- Start on the number 65.
- 34 is 3 tens and 4 units.
- Count on 4 places to add the units.
- Count down 3 rows to add the tens .
- The answer is 99.

Units

1	2	3	4	5	6	7	8	9	10
11	12	13	14	15	16	17	18	19	20
21	22	23	24	25	26	27	28	29	30
31	32	33	34	35	36	37	38	39	40
41	42	43	44	45	46	47	48	49	50
51	52	53	54	55	56	57	58	59	60
61	62	63	64	65	66	67	68	69	70
71	72	73	74	75	76	77	78	79	80
81	82	83	84	85	86	87	88	89	90
91	92	93	94	95	96	97	98	99	100

Tens

Simplifying or partitioning

You can add up by adding up the place values to simplify it and then adding up the totals.

154 + 227

Add the units		$7 + 4 = 11$
Add the tens		$50 + 20 = 70$
Add the hundreds		$100 + 200 = 300$

```
    H   T   U
    3   0   0
        7   0
+       1   1
    _____
    3   8   1
```

 ## Addition with carrying

In this method the sum is completed without simplifying the numbers or using number lines or squares.

Remember! → This is the best method because it is just as good for really, really, big numbers as small ones.

First we will do one that doesn't need any carrying.

627 + 52

The first thing to do is to tidy the sum into place value columns so we can add it up without making any mistakes.
Don't try adding the sum until you have done this.

Real Mathematicians write things down!

You could use graph paper to help you lay the sum out neatly.

```
    H   T   U
    6   2   7
+       5   2
    _____
```

Put a line underneath to separate the sum from the answer. Remember Maths is tidy!

Write the addition sign next to the sum. You might lose a mark in Functional Skills Assessments if you don't show this because it shows you understand what you are doing.

Remember! → Always start by adding the units, the right-hand numbers, first.

Adding the UNITS column

```
    H   T   U
    6   2   7
+       5   2
    _____
            9
```

Write the answer underneath in the same column.

Adding the TENS column

Next add the Tens and write the answer in the tens column.

```
  H  T  U
  6  2  7
+    5  2
---------
     7  9
```

In this sum the numbers are 2 and 5 but look at their place value: they are really worth 20 and 50, but we can call them 2 and 5 because we are only working with the Tens place value column.

Next add the Hundreds. This one is easy as there is only one number, so the answer is 679.

Adding the HUNDREDS column

```
  H  T  U
  6  2  7
+    5  2
---------
  6  7  9
```

Now we will do one with carrying

When numbers add up to more than 9 we have to carry them.
Remember we can't get more than 9 in any of our place value columns.

Here is a tricky example to follow. Don't panic!

857 + 269

First we have to write the sum into place value columns so we can work it out without making any mistakes.
Always do this first in any sum.

```
  H  T  U
  8  5  7
+ 2  6  9
---------
```

Get it sorted

Remember! → Always start by adding the units, the right-hand numbers, first.

In this sum the numbers 7 and 9 add up to 16.

We can't fit more than 9 in any place value column, so here is what to do:

16 is made from one Ten and six Units.
We can put the 6 into the units column, just like we did in the first example, and we carry the 10 by adding it to the Tens column.

Adding the UNITS column

```
  H  T  U
  8  5  7
+ 2  6  9
---------
      ₁ 6
```

Just put a small 1 underneath the sum to remind you to add it in with all the other tens

Next add the tens.
5 + 6 plus + 1 you carried = 12

We can't put more than 9 in any column but 12 is made up from one Ten and two Units.

We can put the 2 in like we did in the first sum and carry the 10 into the next column again.

Hey! These are Tens so why are we calling them 5 and 6 and 2 and why are we carrying a 1 into the Hundreds column?

Remember! → Maths is lazy!

We are working with numbers in the tens column.
We are really adding 50 and 60 and 10; that adds up to 120.

The 20 belongs in the tens column and the hundred is carried across to the Hundreds column.

But it is easier to add small numbers.

We only work with the numbers in each column as we work across the sum. We don't need to worry about them being tens or hundreds if we keep our columns tidy.

```
    H   T   U
    8   5   7
+   2   6   9
        2   6
    1       1
```

Adding the HUNDREDS column

Next add the Hundreds.
8 plus 2 plus 1 makes 11.
11 is one Ten and one Unit.

We can't put more than 9 in the hundreds column, so we need to make a new column on the left.

Put the Unit in as normal and carry the Ten into the new column you just made.

```
  Th  H   T   U
      8   5   7
+     2   6   9
  1,  1   2   6
```

What happens with zeros?

Any time you have a zero it is treated just like any other number. It is there in the place value column and mustn't be ignored. It does a very important job keeping things tidy.

38 + 62

Look at this example

```
    H  T  U
       3  8
+      6  2
    _____
```

Units first, 8 plus 2 is 10.
Mmm, there are no units left to put in the units column in the answer.

We have to use a zero; the zero keeps things tidy.

It tells us there are no units and fills the empty space up for us so we can easily see what the numbers are.

So, put a zero in the units column and carry the Ten.

```
    H  T  U
       3  8
+      6  2
    _____
             0
        1
```

Now add the Tens; 3 plus 6 plus the 1 we carried, makes 10.

No units again, so in goes the zero to keep things tidy for us.

Carry the 1 to the next column like before; it is the only number in the column so we can put it into the answer, 100.

```
    H  T  U
       3  8
+      6  2
    _____
    1  0  0
```

Remember! →

- Always write the sum out correctly in place value columns before starting.
- Always put the addition sign in next to the sum to show what you are doing.
- Always start adding with the Units column.
- Carry numbers across when it adds up to more than 9.
- Write your carried numbers very neatly to help you avoid making mistakes.
- Remember to add in your carried numbers when you add the column up.
- Remember to use Zero the Hero; never leave blank spaces or miss the zero out.

Zero the Hero!

Functional Skills **MATHEMATICS**

Number bonds

One way of adding up more quickly when there are a lot of numbers together is to use number bonds.

Why do I need to know this?
Knowing and recognising number bonds can make adding up and taking away much faster.
It can help you do mental calculations more quickly too.

These are combinations of number 'pairs' that go together to make up a Ten

1	+	9
2	+	8
3	+	7
4	+	6
5	+	5

You might also be able to spot three numbers that make Ten

1	+	1	+	8
2	+	2	+	6
3	+	3	+	4
4	+	4	+	2

If there is a long list of numbers you can **look for number bonds to help you add up more quickly**.

Use a pen or pencil to circle them, tick them or mark them in some way so you can count up the groups of Ten more easily

Here is a list of seven numbers. Look for the number bonds to help you add them up.

$$
\begin{array}{r}
23 \quad \text{---} \quad 3+7 \\
31 \quad \text{---} \quad 1+9 \\
49 \\
27 \\
45 \\
68 \quad \text{---} \quad 8+2 \\
+ \ 82 \\
\hline
5 \\
/ / /
\end{array}
$$

Here you clearly see the number bonds in the Units column.

There are three pairs of number bonds which each add up to Ten and 5 left over, so there is a total of 35 in the Units column.

Every time a Ten is counted, put a little 'tally' line or number 1 under the sum to remind you.

You can write the 5 in and carry the 3. In the example we have used tally lines, but you could write a little 3 there instead.

Do the same in the Tens column

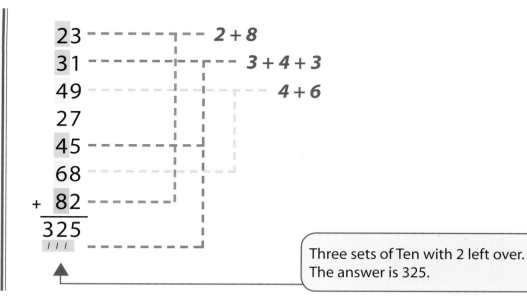

```
  23 - - - - - - - - - 2 + 8
  31 - - - - - - - - - 3 + 4 + 3
  49 - - - - - - - - - 4 + 6
  27
  45
  68
+ 82
 ———
 325
 ///
```

Three sets of Ten with 2 left over. The answer is 325.

Checking your working out

In Functional Skills, when you do a calculation, you need to be able to show you know how to check it has given you the right answer.

There are three main types of check you can use:
- repeat calculations
- reverse checks
- approximate checks

 Repeat calculations

You can do checks by showing a *repeat calculation* and seeing if you get the same answer. This is not the best check because you could make the same mistake twice and not notice.

 Reverse checks

To do a reverse check for an *addition* sum you would have to *take away* one of the numbers in the sum from the answer. This is a good way to do a check but you need to do your subtraction accurately.

The check would be

```
   627              679          679
+   52            -  52        - 627
  ———             ———          ———
  679              627    or     52
```

Remember! The answer in your check must be one of the numbers in the sum you are checking. If it is another number it means you made a mistake in your original calculation.

To reverse check a **subtraction** you would need to **add** the smallest number in the sum onto your answer.

The check would be

```
  6 7 9
-   5 2
  6 2 7
```

```
  6 2 7
+   5 2
  6 7 9
```

Remember! → The answer in your check must be the same as the large number in the sum you are checking. If it is another number it means you made a mistake in your original calculation.

Remember! → If your calculation check shows you have made a mistake, it could be in the original calculation or it could be in your check calculation. Always write sums out neatly with clear place value columns then you are less likely to make a mistake.

→ **Approximate checks**

You can do an approximate check on your calculations by rounding the numbers in the sum to the nearest whole numbers.

```
  6 2 7
+   5 2
  6 7 9
```

| **627** | **rounds to** | **630** |
| **52** | **rounds to** | **50** |

```
  6 3 0
+   5 0
  6 8 0
```

680 is nearly the same as 679 so it shows your answer must be correct. *(This is a good check and you are less likely to make a mistake.)*

"In Functional Skills assessments, try to use different checks."

Remember! →

In Functional Skills Assessments marks are given for checks.

Functional Skills **MATHEMATICS**

Subtraction

Why do I need to know this?
We subtract numbers every day, working out change when shopping, managing a bank account, writing out a customer's bill, and in lots more activities.

There are two ways of subtracting numbers that we have already used in addition. These can be used for subtracting or taking away numbers as well.

Here are some of the words for subtraction:

Subtract   **Minus**
     Take Away   **Fewer**
Decrease   **Difference**

...but they all mean exactly the same thing. Maths can be a bit confusing!

➡ **Number lines**

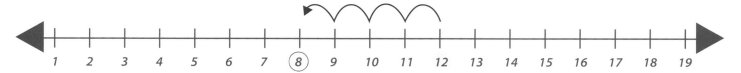

To do this sum   12 – 4

Find the number 12 and count 4 places back along the line to find the answer.

12 - 4 = 8

➡ **Number squares**

Let's try   76 - 24.

First find number 76.

We are taking away 24, Units first, so count back 4 places along the line, to number 72

Now do the Tens.
We are taking away 24.
Count 2 rows up to the smaller numbers.
Remember we are taking this number away so the answer will be smaller.

76 - 24 = 52

Units

1	2	3	4	5	6	7	8	9	10
11	12	13	14	15	16	17	18	19	20
21	22	23	24	25	26	27	28	29	30
31	32	33	34	35	36	37	38	39	40
41	42	43	44	45	46	47	48	49	50
51	52	53	54	55	56	57	58	59	60
61	62	63	64	65	66	67	68	69	70
71	72	73	74	75	76	77	78	79	80
81	82	83	84	85	86	87	88	89	90
91	92	93	94	95	96	97	98	99	100

Tens

➡ Simplifying or partitioning

This is a good method for any number. It is really the same as 'subtraction with borrowing' but divides the numbers into their place value columns first.

173 - 75

We can write this sum as

$$
\begin{array}{r}
100 + 70 + 3 \\
-\ \underline{70 + 5} \\
\end{array}
$$

It is not possible to take 5 away from 3
so the 70 is changed into 60 + 10
and the 10 is put into the units column with the 3.
We can take away the 5 now and put 8 into the answer.

$$
\begin{array}{r}
100 + 60 + 13 \\
-\ \underline{70 + 5} \\
8 \\
\end{array}
$$

Now there is a problem in the Tens column.
70 cannot be taken away from 60.
The 100 is changed to 90 + 10
and the 10 is added to the Tens column.
Now we can finish the sum.

$$
\begin{array}{r}
90 + 70 + 13 \\
-\ \underline{70 + 5} \\
90 + 0 + 8 \\
\end{array}
$$

$1\ 7\ 3 - 7\ 5 = 98$ ➡ $90 + 0 + 8 = 98$

➡ Subtraction with borrowing

Now we will learn one of the best methods for subtraction.

> **This is one of the best methods because it works for every number - even really big ones!**

It sounds confusing but borrowing is a bit like carrying:
we just need to keep things tidy!

First we will practise one without any borrowing.

The sum is written out in columns, just the same
as in an addition sum, so 177 – 32 looks like this.

$1\ 7\ 7 - 32$ ➡

$$
\begin{array}{r}
\text{H T U} \\
1\ 7\ 7 \\
-\ \underline{3\ 2} \\
\end{array}
$$

Functional Skills **MATHEMATICS**

The Units, Tens and Hundreds are written neatly in columns. Maths is Tidy! Remember to write in the minus sign to show you understand what you are doing.

The numbers in the sum are 177 and 32. When we are doing our working out we always take the smallest number away from the biggest number.

> **Take Care!**
> **Always write the biggest number at the top of your sum.**
> **Never take away a top number from a bottom number.**

To help us remember we will use a different colour for each number. We will take the red number away from the green one.

Subtract the UNITS

H	T	U
1	7	7
-	3	2

Units first, take the **2** away from the **7**; that leaves **5**.

H	T	U
1	7	7
-	3	2
		5

Now the Tens column: **7** take away **3**; that leaves **4**.

Subtract the TENS

H	T	U
1	7	7
-	3	2
	4	5

Now the Hundreds column. We're lucky, there is nothing to take away from the **1** so we still have the hundred in that column and can put the **1** straight into the answer.

Subtract the HUNDREDS

H	T	U
1	7	7
-	3	2
1	4	5

The answer is 145

> 1 7 7 - 32 = 145

Remember Checks!

We can do a simple check here to see if our answer could be right.
We had 177 and we took 32 away, so the answer should be smaller than 177.
The answer is 145. This is smaller than 177 by about 30, so it should be right.

Now we will look at borrowing.

Lots of people find this very confusing.
Don't panic! It's easy when you keep things Tidy!

First, a not too tricky one...

183 - 75

Write it into place value columns with the big number on the top.
We will use colours in the practice sums to show which number is at the top and which number is at the bottom.

```
  H   T   U
  1   8   3
-     7   5
```

Subtract the UNITS

Start with the Units, **3** take away **5**   ...Impossible!

We can't do this, but we are taking the number **75** away from the number **183** so *we have to find a way of making it possible*.

Borrowing

The way to solve this problem is to **borrow** from the next column.
We **borrow** ten from the Tens column and squeeze it into the units column to help the **3** out.

```
  H   T   U
  1  ⁷8̸ ¹3
-     7   5
```

In the sum we have put a little line through the **8** in the Tens column.
(It is really 80 because it is 8 Tens. We just call it 8 to be lazy).

Next to the **8** we write 7, because we have borrowed one and 8 take away 1 leaves 7.
Now we squeeze the ten we borrowed into the units column next to the **3**, to help it out. With the 3 already in the units column plus the 10 we borrowed we now have 13.

13 Take away **5** leaves 8, so we write that into the answer.

```
  H   T   U
  1  ⁷8̸ ¹3
-     7   5
          8
```

Subtract the TENS

Next we do the Tens column. 7 take away 7 leaves us with nothing.
We can't just leave it blank, so we need an important number to help us fill this space.

```
  H  T  U
  1  ⁷8̸ ¹3
-    7  5
─────────
     0  8
```

...call for

Zero the Hero!

Even though we have no Tens we must put a zero in to show there are no Tens and to keep all our columns tidy.

Subtract the HUNDREDS

Now in the Hundreds column there is nothing to take away from the 1 so we can put that into the answer.

```
  H  T  U
  1  ⁷8̸ ¹3
-    7  5
─────────
  1  0  8
```

...the answer is 108

OK, let's try a harder sum with more borrowing.

462 - 163

First, write it into place value columns.
Never try and do a sum until you have written it out and made it tidy!

Remember! → # Real mathematicians write things down!

Big Number on the top remember.

```
  H  T  U
  4  6  2
-  1  6  3
─────────
```

Subtract the UNITS

Always start with the Units.
In this sum we have **2** take away **3**

...Impossible

We can't do this, but we are taking the number **163** away from the number **462** so **we have to find a way of making it possible**.

We learned in the last sum that we have to **borrow** from the next column. We **borrow** ten from the Tens column and squeeze it into the units column to help the 2 out.

```
  H  T  U
  4  ⁵6̸ ¹2
-  1  6  3
─────────
```

In the sum we have put a little line through the 6 in the Tens column. (It is really a 60 because it is 6 Tens. We just call it 6 to make it easier).

Next to the **6** we write 5, because we have borrowed one and 6 take away 1 leaves 5.
Now we squeeze the ten we borrowed into the units column next to the **2**, to help it out. With the 2 already in the units column plus the 10 we borrowed we now have 12.
That's possible to do now.

12 take away **3** leaves 9.

```
        H    T    U
        4   ⁵6̸  ¹2
    -   1    6    3
                  9
```

Subtract the TENS

Now the Tens column.
Now we have borrowed one to help us with the units we have **5** take away **6**.

Oh dear, we can't do that and we can **never take the top number away from the bottom number** because the sum we are working out is **462 – 163**.

The answer is **borrow** from the next column.

```
        H    T    U
      ³4̸  ¹⁵6̸  ¹2
    -   1    6    3
                  9
```

4 take away 1 is 3. Put a neat small line through the 4 and write a little 3 next to it, to show we have borrowed one of the Hundreds to help in the sum.

Then squeeze the extra 1 we borrowed into the Tens column, next to the 5 we have there already. This gives us 15 in the Tens column.

> **Hang on! I know what you are thinking... these are Hundreds and Tens so how do we end up saying we have got 15?**
>
> What we have really done is borrow a 100 from the Hundreds column and squeezed it in to the Tens column with the 50 we already have making 150. Take a look at the place value columns.
>
> It is easier to add small numbers so we just work with the numbers in each column as we work across. We don't need to worry about them being tens or hundreds if we keep our columns tidy.

Subtract the TENS

Back to the sum.
15 take away 6 leaves 9. Write this into the answer box.

```
       H   T   U
     ³ 4  ¹⁵ 6  ¹ 2
  -    1   6   3
       _____
           9   9
```

Subtract the HUNDREDS

That just leaves the Hundreds column 3 take away 1 leaves 2.

```
       H   T   U
     ³ 4  ¹⁵ 6  ¹ 2
  -    1   6   3
       _____
       2   9   9
```

...the answer is 299

By keeping things tidy and borrowing when we got stuck we got the right answer.

This was a **SUPER TRICKY** example.
If you can do this sum you can do **ANY** take away sum.

Remember! →

Always write the sum out correctly in place value columns before starting.
Always have the biggest number at the top.
Always put the subtraction sign in next to the sum to show what you are doing.
Always start with the Units column.
Never take a top number from a bottom number however big or small they are!
Borrow from the next column when you haven't got enough numbers to do your take away.
Cross out numbers and write in the new value very neatly to help you avoid mistakes.
Remember, borrowing can happen in more than one column so don't panic!
Remember to use 'Zero the Hero' as he does a very important job for us.

Zero the Hero!

Times tables

Knowing your tables helps you do calculations much more quickly and helps you become more confident with all your maths.

Why do I need to know this?
Times tables are the most useful things to learn because they help with everything. It makes working things out really quick!

 Tables square

Here is a times tables square that goes up to **10 x 10**

	1	2	3	4	5	6	7	8	9	10
1	1	2	3	4	5	6	7	8	9	10
2	2	4	6	8	10	12	14	16	18	20
3	3	6	9	12	15	18	21	24	27	30
4	4	8	12	16	20	24	28	32	36	40
5	5	10	15	20	25	30	35	40	45	50
6	6	12	18	24	30	36	42	48	54	60
7	7	14	21	28	35	42	49	56	63	70
8	8	16	24	32	40	48	56	64	72	80
9	9	18	27	36	45	54	63	72	81	90
10	10	20	30	40	50	60	70	80	90	100

This looks like an awful lot of numbers to learn, but let's look more closely...

Nearly half the table is shaded. That is because when we multiply numbers together it doesn't matter which one comes first.

| 4 x 3 |
| or |
| 3 x 4 |

= **12**

| 2 x 3 x 5 |
| or |
| 5 x 2 x 3 |
| or |
| 3 x 5 x 2 |

= **30**

You can try some more for yourself.
This means that if we learn 4 x 5, we don't have to learn 5 x 4, because the answer is the same.

Nearly half the squares are like this so we can shade them to show we don't need to learn them.

Remember! →

Knowing your times tables is one of the *most important* things you can do to improve your maths and help you get better marks in a Functional Skills test.

Most people find the 1, 2 and 5 times tables quite easy to learn or to quickly count up on their fingers.

The ten times table is also easy: you just add a zero.

5 x 10	=	50
7 x 10	=	70
9 x 10	=	90

All the easiest numbers are coloured blue

	1	2	3	4	5	6	7	8	9	10
1	1	2	3	4	5	6	7	8	9	10
2	2	4	6	8	10	12	14	16	18	20
3	3	6	9	12	15	18	21	24	27	30
4	4	8	12	16	20	24	28	32	36	40
5	5	10	15	20	25	30	35	40	45	50
6	6	12	18	24	30	36	42	48	54	60
7	7	14	21	28	35	42	49	56	63	70
8	8	16	24	32	40	48	56	64	72	80
9	9	18	27	36	45	54	63	72	81	90
10	10	20	30	40	50	60	70	80	90	100

➡ Square numbers

Examples

A really useful set of numbers to learn are the **Square Numbers**.
These are numbers that come from two numbers multiplied by themselves.

| 2 x 2 = 4 | 4 x 4 = 16 | 6 x 6 = 36 |

They are called **Square Numbers** because if you draw a grid it makes a square. The Square Number is the total number of squares in the grid.

4 x 4 =

	1	2	3	4
1	1	2	3	4
2	2	4	6	8
3	3	6	9	12
4	4	8	12	16

1	2	3	4
5	6	7	8
9	10	11	12
13	14	15	16

$6 \times 6 =$

	1	2	3	4	5	6
1	1	2	3	4	5	6
2	2	4	6	8	10	12
3	3	6	9	12	15	18
4	4	8	12	16	20	24
5	5	10	15	20	25	30
6	6	12	18	24	30	36

1	2	3	4	5	6
7	8	9	10	11	12
13	14	15	16	17	18
19	20	21	22	23	24
25	26	27	28	29	30
31	32	33	34	35	36

Some of the Square Numbers are already *coloured blue* in the tables square so there are only 6 left to learn. The square numbers are coloured pink and make the diagonal line in the grid.

My favourite Square Number is 36. What's yours?

	1	2	3	4	5	6	7	8	9	10
1	1	2	3	4	5	6	7	8	9	10
2	2	4	6	8	10	12	14	16	18	20
3	3	6	9	12	15	18	21	24	27	30
4	4	8	12	16	20	24	28	32	36	40
5	5	10	15	20	25	30	35	40	45	50
6	6	12	18	24	30	36	42	48	54	60
7	7	14	21	28	35	42	49	56	63	70
8	8	16	24	32	40	48	56	64	72	80
9	9	18	27	36	45	54	63	72	81	90
10	10	20	30	40	50	60	70	80	90	100

The 3 and 4 times tables are the next easiest to learn. They are *coloured yellow*. There are only 9 of these left to learn because we already know the two square numbers.

If you can't remember your 3 and 4 times tables you can still count these up quite quickly on your fingers when you are doing a sum.

Functional Skills **MATHEMATICS**

The only really tricky ones are **coloured in red**. These are a bit harder to remember but there are only 6 of them to learn because we already know the four square numbers.

Wise Up to **Easy Times**

So, learning your times tables is not really as hard as it first looks is it?

Draw your own grid and colour in the ones you need to practise learning.

Remember! ➡

This is the **most important** bit of maths to help you do better in your Functional Skills test.

➡ **Multiples and patterns**

When we count up by adding the same number on each time we call it a Multiple.
We can use multiples for counting upwards or for finding what number a number can be divided by.

Let's start with multiples of 2.
Any even number is a multiple of 2.
Any even number can be divided by 2 as well.

Multiples of **2**   **2, 4, 6, 8, 10, 12, 14, 16, 18, 20, 22, 24, 26, 28, 30, 32...**

Multiples of 5 are also easy to spot.
Any number that ends in 5 or 0 is a multiple of 5.
These numbers can also be divided by 5.

Multiples of **5**   **5, 10, 15, 20, 25, 30, 35, 40, 45, 50, 55, 60, 65, 70, 75...**

Multiples of 10 are the easiest of all.
They all end in zero.
Any number that ends in zero can be divided by 10.

Multiples of **10**   **10, 20, 30, 40, 50, 60, 70, 80, 90, 100...**

When you learn your times tables you will learn to count up in 3s, 4s, 5s, 6s, 7s, 8s, 9s, and 10s. Each series of numbers are multiples of that number.

Multiples of 3

For example in the 3 times table we see

3, 6, 9, 12, 15, 18, 21, 24, 27, 30...

Each of these numbers in the 3 times table is a multiple of 3.
Each of these numbers can also be divided by 3.

Multiples of 8

In the 8 times table we see

8, 16, 24, 32, 40, 48, 56, 64, 72, 80...

Each of these numbers in the 8 times table is a multiple of 8.
Each of these numbers can also be divided by 8.

Remember! → Multiples of any number can also be divided by the same number. This will be useful to know when you are doing division.

Number patterns

The numbers in each times table make a regular pattern.

	1	2	3	4	5	6	7	8	9	10
1	1	2	3	4	5	6	7	8	9	10
2	2	4	6	8	10	12	14	16	18	20
3	3	6	9	12	15	18	21	24	27	30
4	4	8	12	16	20	24	28	32	36	40
5	5	10	15	20	25	30	35	40	45	50
6	6	12	18	24	30	36	42	48	54	60
7	7	14	21	28	35	42	49	56	63	70
8	8	16	24	32	40	48	56	64	72	80
9	9	18	27	36	45	54	63	72	81	90
10	10	20	30	40	50	60	70	80	90	100

Functional Skills **MATHEMATICS**

Multiplying

Just like the subtraction section, there is more than one word for Multiply. Here are just a few: 'Times'; 'by'; 'product'; 'lots of'; 'multiple of'; they all mean exactly the same thing.

There are many different ways of multiplying but we will look at three of the most common methods.

They all work well and you should use the method you are most confident with.

Why do I need to know this?
We multiply things every day, working out costs, working out how much we have been paid, buying carpet or wallpaper, using recipes, working out weekly costs and many more activities.

In the **Grid Method** a grid is drawn. Each section is worked out separately and added up at the end to give the answer.

→ Grid method

The Grid we use is small because in maths we like to make things easier, but it really represents a bigger grid showing the area.

On the next page there is an example of what a big grid would look like if we drew it out in full, then we will see how we can make that sum into a smaller grid we can easily manage.

23 x 12
Using a full grid

A grid is used to show a rectangle 23 squares by 12 squares.

The numbers are split into their Tens and Units and written next to the grid.

> 10 and 2 make 12.
> 20 and 3 make 23.

The first number (23) has been written next to the side of the grid and the second number (12) has been written across the top of the grid.

You can see where the lines divide the grid that there is the same number of squares as the value written next to it.

We work out the area, or number of squares in each section. Colours have been used to help you to match the sums to the areas on the grid.

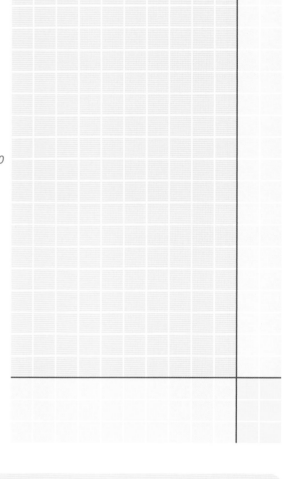

Splitting the answer into sections

20 x 10 = 200

20 x 2 = 40

3 x 10 = 30

> The answers are the same as the number of squares in each section of the grid. Try counting them for yourself!

3 x 2 = 6

All we do to find the answer to 23 x 12 is to add these answers up.

The final answer calculation

```
    2  0  0
       4  0
       3  0
+         6
   ─────────
    2  7  6
```

This is a good method but we can't draw a big full-sized grid for every sum, so because it's maths we make things simpler for ourselves by drawing a simple grid with all the squares the same size.

23 x 12
Using a small grid

We write the answers for each section into each box and add the totals up at the side of the grid.

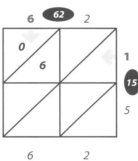

	10	2
20	200	40
3	30	6

```
  H T U
    2 4 0
  +   3 6
  -------
    2 7 6
```

> Take care to line up your Hundreds, Tens and Units before you add them up.

➡ Lattice method

The Lattice method looks a little bit like the Grid method but is really quite different because it can't be drawn as a big grid of squares.

Each of the Lattice boxes are divided diagonally with a space at the top for Tens and a space at the bottom for Units.

Space for Tens

Space for Units

62 x 15

Let's see how it works on this sum...

Break it into sections

We need a box for each of the numbers in the sum.
We draw a grid: two boxes across and two boxes down.

6 x 1

The first number (62) is written across the top, and the second number (15) is written down the side. Starting with the top row multiply 6 x 1 and put the answer into the lattice below 6.

Notice that the answer is 6 Units so we put Zero in the Tens space to show there is nothing there.

2 x 1

6 x 5

2 x 5

Then on the same row work out 2 x 1.
Next 6 x 5 and 2 x 5 for the bottom row in the lattice.

6 x 1 = 6	2 x 1 = 2
6 x 5 = 30	2 x 5 = 10

Remember! ➡ Tens go into the top part above the diagonal line.

The final answer

To work out the answer we add the numbers along the diagonal stripes, starting on the right hand side, just as in ordinary addition.
The answer is 930.

What happened to the zero?
It is in front of all the numbers.
We aren't using that place value so we don't need it in the answer.

Functional Skills **MATHEMATICS**

We will do another sum now to see what happens when the diagonal stripes add up to more than 9.
Just like the place value columns in addition sums we can only go up to 9 in any of the diagonal stripes.

We will also try a bigger number to show how to draw a bigger lattice.

175 x 15

Break it into sections

First draw the lattice. This time we need an extra set of boxes on our lattice because the number has three digits in it.

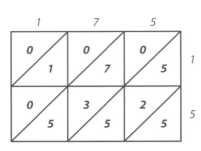

Top Row	Bottom Row
1 x 1 = 1	1 x 5 = 5
7 x 1 = 7	7 x 5 = 35
5 x 1 = 5	5 x 5 = 25

Now multiply each of the top row numbers with the 1 from the 15. Then the bottom row numbers with the 5.

Now start adding up the diagonals, starting with the right hand bottom corner.

What if a diagonal adds up to more than 9?

Oops! The pink diagonal adds up to 12.

We know we can only have numbers up to 9 in an addition column.

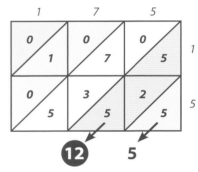

So we write in the 2 and carry the Ten across to the next diagonal by putting a little number 1 in the white section ready to add with the other numbers. It is exactly the same as when we do normal addition.

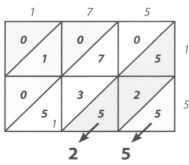

The same thing happens in the white section. The total is 16, so we carry the 1 across to the blue diagonal.
Write the Units number in and carry the Tens across to the next diagonal section.

The final answer

Work neatly then you won't make mistakes and you won't lose marks in the assessment.
The answers is 2,625

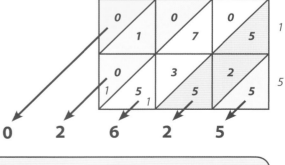

Th	H	T	U	The Zero from the yellow section is in front of the other
0	2	6	2	5	numbers so it can be ignored as we don't use this place value.

Long multiplication

Long multiplication
is good because it works
for numbers of all sizes.

This method is one
of the most common
methods used.

The sum is laid out using the place value columns we have already learned
about in addition and subtraction.

Never try and do a multiplication in your head.

**Real mathematicians
write things down!**

You will do **LOTS** of writing.
Keep your handwriting **VERY** neat.
Mathematicians use piles of paper.

62 x 13

The sum is

```
    6  2
x   1  3
```

Write the sum out like this; we put the
multiplication sign in to show we are
multiplying.

We multiply the bottom number with the top number, one number at a time
and add the results to get the answer, just like the Grid and Lattice methods.

*Multiplying
by the Unit*

```
    T  U
    6  2
x   1  3
       6
```

Start with the Unit on the bottom; in this sum it is the
number **3**. Multiply this with the top number, starting
with the top Unit; in this sum that is number **2**.

3 x 2 = 6 We write this in our answer
under the units column.

```
    T  U
    6  2
x   1  3
 1  8  6
```

Next we multiply the same **3** with the number in the top
Tens column; in this sum it is number **6**.

3 x 6 = 18 We can't have a number
bigger than 9 in any column so when
we write in our answer the 8 is
written in as usual and the 1 is carried
across to the Hundreds column.

Remember! →

It doesn't matter that we don't have a Hundreds column.
If we need extra columns as answers get larger we can just add them in.
The important thing is to keep the place value columns tidy.

Take care!

```
      T  U
      6  2
  x   1  3
     ‾‾‾‾‾‾
   1  8  6
```

186 is not the final answer; this is only the first part using the bottom Unit to multiply with all the digits in the top number. There is still the bottom Ten to multiply with.

Remember! →

When we worked out 3 x 6, this was really 3 x 60 as the 6 is in the Tens column. So although our answer was 18, the real value is 180.
That is why we can put the 1 into the Hundreds column.

Maths is Lazy!
To make things easier in maths we can just say 3 x 6 = 18.

Multiplying by the Ten

This time we multiply the top number, 62, with the Tens value in the bottom number. In this sum this is 1.

```
      T  U
      6  2
  x   1  3
     ‾‾‾‾‾‾
   1  8  6
         0
```

The important thing to do first is to put a zero into the units column.

We do this because the number 1 is not one Unit, it is really one Ten, so we can't use the Units column for any part of the answer.
Zero fills the space to remind us and to make the answer right.

Zero the Hero!

```
      T  U
      6  2
  x   1  3
     ‾‾‾‾‾‾
   1  8  6
      2  0
```

Using the top number we start with the Units again.
1 x 2 = 2.

The answer goes under the Tens column and the 1 is then multiplied with the next number.

```
      T  U
      6  2
  x   1  3
     ‾‾‾‾‾‾
   1  8  6
 + 6  2  0
```

1 x 6 = 6.

We write the 6 into the answer making sure the digits are tidy in their place value columns.
Then we can add them up more easily.

We draw a line under the two parts we have worked out and add them up just like a normal addition sum. We are only adding our results, in this sum
186 + 620.

The final answer

Check your working

		T	U
		6	2
x		1	3
	1	8	6
+	6	2	0
	8	0	6
		1	

Don't forget to check your answers.

Use a calculator the do a *reverse check*.

806 ÷ 13   or   806 ÷ 62

 Remember! → If your numbers add up to 10, 20 or any number with a zero, you must put the zero into the column to show there is no number there.

 Remember! → Always write the sum out neatly in place value columns.
Always start with the Units column.
Put a Zero in to the Units place before you start working with the Tens.
Carry numbers across when they are bigger than 9.
Add columns to the left if the answer gets too big.

Long Multiplication can
be a bit long and tricky sometimes,
so if you followed this example all the
way through first time...

Well Done!

Dividing

There are several ways of doing division; we are going to look at two of them.

Chunking and *Short division*

There are different words for dividing. The most common ones are:

Sharing   **Division**
          Going 'in to'

When you know your times tables it is easy to do simple division in your head.

Division is Multiplication in reverse!

If you know that **3 x 2 = 6**

3 + 3 + 3 = 3 3 3

Then you can easily work out that **6 ÷ 2 = 3**

3 3 3 = ⃝⃝⃝ + ⃝⃝⃝

Sometimes it is too difficult to do it in your head and you need to use a written method to find the answer.

➡ Chunking

This method is called chunking because we work out the answer by subtracting multiples of the number in chunks.

It can be used on both big and small numbers.

First we write out the sum ready to solve it. Division sums are written like this...

198 ÷ 6

Place the number we are dividing by at the front of the sum. ➡ 6⟌198

Remember! ➡ Maths is a bit lazy so we don't want to do more work than we need to do. By finding the nearest multiples first, we can get to the answer more quickly.

Work out <u>roughly</u> how big the answer will be	We do this by multiplying 6 by 10, 20 or more to find the two multiples that 'trap' the number 198.

6 x 10 = 60
6 x 20 = 120
6 x 30 = 180 ⟵　180 is less than 198 but...
6 x 40 = 240 ⟵　240 is more than 198.

We know the answer to 198 ÷ 6 will be **between 30 and 40.**

We can start by subtracting 180 from 198 and writing 6 x 30 next to the sum to remind us that 6 divided into 180 exactly 30 times.

```
6 ) 1 9 8
  - 1 8 0     6 x 30
    ─────
      1 8
```

We have 18 left over so we need to find out how many times 6 will divide into 18.
Last time we used 10, 20, 30 because 198 is a big number.
18 is a smaller number so we can use single numbers.

6 x 1 = 6
6 x 2 = 12
6 x 3 = 18 ⟵　This is the value we want.

We subtract it from our sum and write 6 x 3 next to the sum again to show 6 divided into 18 exactly 3 times.

The final calculation

```
6 ) 1 9 8
  - 1 8 0     6 x 30
    ─────
      1 8           30 + 3 = 33      The answer is 33.
  -   1 8     6 x  3
    ─────
        0
```

Sometimes the answer is not an exact number...

154 ÷ 5	First write the sum out ready to solve it...

```
5 ) 1 5 4
```

Next use multiples to 'trap' the number 154.

Work out <u>roughly</u> how big the answer will be	**5 x 10 = 50** **5 x 20 = 100** **5 x 30 = 150** ⟵　150 is smaller than 154 but... **5 x 40 = 200** ⟵　200 is more than 154.

Now we know the answer is **between 30 and 40**.

We can subtract 150 and write 5 x 30 next to the sum to show what we are doing.

```
        3 0   r 4
    5 ) 1 5 4
    -   1 5 0      5 x 30
            4
```

We have 4 left. This is less than 5 so we cannot subtract any more.

The answer is 30 remainder 4.

This is maths and maths is lazy so we write 'r' instead of 'remainder'.

30 r 4

➡️ **Short division**

129 ÷ 3

The sum is written out in the same way as for chunking.

Short division works well if you are dividing with small numbers.

```
3 ) 129
```

In short division you divide the number and write the answer across the top.

Step 1

```
3 ) 1 2 9
```

1 divided by 3. This can't be done so we move across and use 12 divided by 3.

```
3 ) 1 2 9
```

$12 \div 3 = 4$

```
      4
3 ) 1 2 9
```

Write the 4 on the top line, above the 2 because this is the last number we were working with.

Step 2

```
      4
3 ) 1 2 9
```

Now divide 3 into the next digit, 9.

$9 \div 3 = 3$

```
      4 3
3 ) 1 2 9
```

Write the 3 on the top line, above the 9.

The answer is 43.

Let's do a slightly harder one...

$9,809 \div 7$

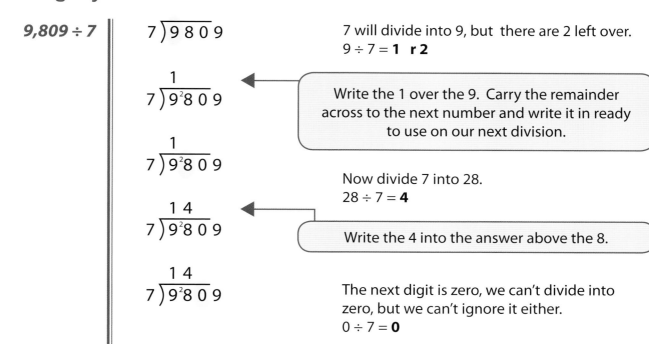

$7\overline{)9\ 8\ 0\ 9}$

7 will divide into 9, but there are 2 left over.
$9 \div 7 = \mathbf{1}\ \mathbf{r\,2}$

$\begin{array}{r} 1 \\ 7\overline{)9\,{}^{2}8\ 0\ 9} \end{array}$

Write the 1 over the 9. Carry the remainder across to the next number and write it in ready to use on our next division.

$\begin{array}{r} 1 \\ 7\overline{)9\,{}^{2}8\ 0\ 9} \end{array}$

Now divide 7 into 28.
$28 \div 7 = \mathbf{4}$

$\begin{array}{r} 1\ 4 \\ 7\overline{)9\,{}^{2}8\ 0\ 9} \end{array}$

Write the 4 into the answer above the 8.

$\begin{array}{r} 1\ 4 \\ 7\overline{)9\,{}^{2}8\ 0\ 9} \end{array}$

The next digit is zero, we can't divide into zero, but we can't ignore it either.
$0 \div 7 = \mathbf{0}$

Remember! ➡ Always write the zero in place to make the answer right.

$\begin{array}{r} 1\ 4\ 0 \\ 7\overline{)9\,{}^{2}8\ 0\ 9} \end{array}$

Write the 0 into the answer.

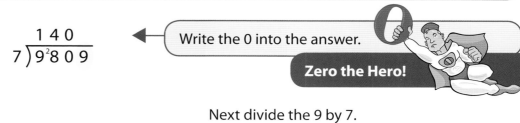

Zero the Hero!

Next divide the 9 by 7.
$9 \div 7 = \mathbf{1\ r\,2}$

$\begin{array}{r} 1\ 4\ 0\ 1\ \ r\,2 \\ 7\overline{)9\,{}^{2}8\ 0\ 9} \end{array}$

We can write the 1 in above the 9 and write the remainder next to the answer.

The answer is 1,401 r 2.

Rounding and estimating

In Functional Skills it is very useful to be able to estimate something.

Why do I need to know this?

This is important in Functional Skills because you need to use it when checking your work.

It helps us every day too when handling money, measuring things and working out a rough idea of something's value.

Estimating is another way of saying guessing, but when estimating we try to use any information we have to make our estimate or guess more accurate.

Estimating helps us when we do calculation checks to see if our answer seems about right.

We use estimating often in everyday life.

At the supermarket we might estimate what the final bill will be to see if we have enough money.

When we estimate we usually use rounding first to help us be more accurate.

➡ Rounding

Rounding is when we make a number simpler so we can work things out more quickly or easily.

There is a rule we use for rounding numbers.

➡ The Rounding Rule

Find the place value you want to round to:
If the number to the right is 0, 1, 2, 3 or 4 (less than 5), the place value number stays the same.
If the number to the right is 5, 6, 7, 8 or 9 (5 or more), the place value number goes up by 1.

Functional Skills **MATHEMATICS**

➡ Rounding to the nearest ten, hundred or thousand

Sometimes you will be asked to round a number to the nearest ten, hundred or thousand.
To do this you need to use place value columns and the Rounding Rule.

When you have finished rounding, the smaller place values will have zeros in them.

Rounding to the nearest Ten

1,219
to the nearest Ten

We will round this number to the nearest Ten.
In this example we will highlight the Tens and Units columns.
Tens is the place value we want to round to.

Th	H	T	U
1	2	1	9

Now look at the Units.
In this example, the Unit is 9.

If the Unit is 5, 6, 7, 8 or 9 we always round the Ten up to the next number.

So now we look again at the Tens; in this number the unit is 1.
The next number will be 2.
We put a 2 in the Tens column and a zero in the Units column.

1,219 rounded to the nearest ten will be 1,220.

Th	H	T	U
1	2	2	0

Zero is put in the Units column because we are not using that column. We are working to the nearest Ten.

Look at the highlighted Tens and Units columns in the original number.
The number is 19. This is much closer to 20 than 10.
This is why the Ten was increased from 1 to 2.

1,424
to the nearest Ten

Now another number to the nearest Ten...

Th	H	T	U
1	4	2	4

The Unit in this number is 4.

If the Unit number is 1, 2, 3 or 4 the Tens number will stay the same because it is still nearest to that Ten.
We put a zero in the Units column and don't change the Ten.

1,424 rounded to the nearest ten will be 1,420.

Th	H	T	U
1	4	2	0

Zero is put in the Units column because we are not using that column. We are working to the nearest Ten.

Look at the highlighted Tens and Units columns in the original number.
24 is much nearer to 20 than 30.
This is why the Tens number doesn't change.

What about the nearest Hundred?

1,424
to the nearest Hundred

Th	H	T	U
1	4	2	4

This works exactly the same but this time we look at just the Hundreds and Tens columns.

Hundreds is the place value we want to round to.
Tens is the place value we need to look at first. The Ten is 2, so we don't change the Hundred.
If the Tens number is 1, 2, 3 or 4 the Hundreds number will stay the same because it is still nearest to that Hundred.

We put a zero in the Tens column and the Units column and leave the Thousand column the same.

1,424 rounded to the nearest hundred will be 1,400.

Th	H	T	U
1	4	0	0

This time we are not using the Tens or the Units place value columns so they both have a zero in them.

Let's do the nearest Thousand...

4,817
to the nearest Thousand

Th	H	T	U
4	8	1	7

The Hundreds is 8. This is big enough to increase the next column by 1. We put a zero in the Hundreds, Tens and Units columns and increase the Thousands column from 4 to 5.

4,817 rounded to the nearest thousand will be 5,000.

Th	H	T	U
5	0	0	0

There are zeros in the other place value columns because we are not using them.

➡ Rounding with decimals

Sometimes we want to round to the nearest whole number from a decimal number.
This uses the same Rounding Rule.

125.6
to the nearest whole number

Let's round this number to the nearest whole number...

H	T	U		
1	2	5	.	6

The nearest whole number in a decimal is always the Units column.

Units is the place value we want to round to.
Look at the number to the right.
It is 6. This is more than 5 so the Unit value increases by 1.

The rounded number is 126 to the nearest whole number.

Here is another one to try...

2,354.376
to the nearest whole number

2 , 3 5 4 . 3 7 6

This number looks more difficult but the rule is the same.
First find the Unit column.

2 , 3 5 4 . 3 7 6

The next number to the right is 3. This is less than 5 so the unit value stays the same.

The rounded number is 2,354 to the nearest whole number.

 In Functional Skills you will also be expected to understand how to round numbers to 2 decimal places.

In Maths, 2 decimal places is written as 2 dp, for short. Mathematicians like to shorten things.

Rounding in decimals works exactly the same as when rounding with whole numbers. We will try a few to see.

The Rounding Rule is the same as for whole numbers.

127.256
to 2 dp

Let's look at some decimal numbers and round them to 2 dp...

H	T	U	.	1/10	1/100	1/1000
1	2	7	.	3	5	6

We only want 2 decimal places. This means the first 2 place value columns after the decimal point.
These are the decimal Tenths and Hundredths columns.

We always want the Hundredths column as our last column to keep; in this number the smallest place value we want to have is the 5.

We look at the number to the right; this is the first column we want to get rid of. It is 6. This is more than 5 so the Hundredths column we want to keep goes up by 1.

```
H   T   U   .   1/10   1/100
1   2   7   .   3      6
```

We only want to keep 2 decimal places so any other columns to the right are left off the answer.

The rounded number is 127.36 to 2 dp.

Now try this one...

2 7 . 0 3 4 5 9

27. 03459
to the nearest whole number

It looks more difficult because it has a zero in and has 5 decimal places. Don't panic; the rule is just the same as before.

Find the Hundredths column.

2 7 . 0 3 4 5 9

The place value to the right is 4.
This is less than 5 so the Hundredths column stays the same.

The rounded number is 27.03 to 2 dp.

➡ Estimating

Let's see how rounding is used in estimating amounts.
We can estimate and round distances, time, weight, totals of sums, or anything else that we can calculate.

Distance

Distance is measured in metres and kilometres.

An example:
If you are going to visit a friend who lives 9 kilometres away, to **estimate the total distance of your journey there and back** you can round 9 kilometres to the nearest 10 kilometres.

10 + 10 = 20 km
This is close to the actual distance of 18 km.

Functional Skills **MATHEMATICS**

Money

If soup is **47p a tin** and we buy **4 tins** we can quickly estimate our bill by rounding the cost of the soup to a whole number that is easy to add.

47p is rounded to 50p, and because there are 100 pence in £1 that makes it easy to add up. 50p x 4 = £2.

We know we need a few pence less than £2 to buy 4 tins at 47p each.

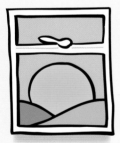

We rounded 47p to the nearest 50p.

We need to **round to a number close to the number we are working with.**

If we rounded the 47p tins to £1 our estimate would be a long way from the true value. £1 x 4 = £4.

This is called an **Appropriate Level** of accuracy.

Remember! ➔ The closer our rounded value is to the number we are working with the more accurate our estimates or calculations will be.

Length

Length is measured in millimetres, centimetres and metres.

You can round to any close value that is appropriate for the sum you are working out.

This can be the nearest millimetre, centimetre, 10 centimetres, metre or any other appropriate value.

An example:
A window is **158 cm x 225 cm**. So that you can choose curtains to fit you need to **round up to the nearest 10 cm**.

158 cm rounded to the nearest 10 is 160 cm.
225 cm rounded to the nearest 10 is 230 cm.

Time

Time is measured in years, months, weeks, days, hours, minutes and seconds.

An example:
If it takes 18 minutes to walk to the shops and 27 minutes to do the shopping, **how long does the shopping trip take**?

This question uses minutes so you can round to the nearest 5 minutes to make it easier to add.

18 minutes can be rounded to 20 minutes.

27 minutes is almost 30 minutes which is half an hour.

20 + 30 + 20 = 70 minutes

There are 60 minutes in an hour so it takes approximately 1 hour and 10 minutes to do the shopping.

Functional Skills **MATHEMATICS**

→ Estimating in checks

When you are checking calculations you can also use rounding to estimate your answer.

Checking the calculation
27 + 39 = 66

In this sum we will round to the nearest Ten.

27 + 39 = 66 | 27 rounds to 30 | | 39 rounds to 40 |

30 + 40 = 70, so the answer of 66 must be about right.

> In calculation checks, and in everyday life, when we round numbers to estimate calculations we sometimes have decimals. This is most true when working with money.

Estimating the total price

We have 4 items on a shopping list and the prices are:

| £3.40 | + | £1.50 | + | £0.68 | + | £2.00 |

To estimate the total we could round the numbers to whole £s.

Using the Rounding Rule...

£3.40 = £3 because the 4 is less than 5.
£1.50 = £2 because the next place value is 5 or more.
£0.68 = £1 because the next place value is 5 or more.
£2.00 = £2 no pence to round here.
£3 + £2 + £1 + £2 = 8

So the **estimated total is £8**.
The **actual total is £7.58** so the estimate is quite close.

Rounding to the nearest 10p

You could choose to round to the nearest 10p, which would be even more accurate. This will be easier if you are familiar with number bonds to help you add up the totals. Look at these prices...

| £2.75 | + | £3.47 | + | £6.72 |

We want to keep the Tenths column, the Hundredths column is 5, which is 5 or more, so the Tenths column goes up by 1. The answer is **£2.80**.

We are looking at the 7. This is more than 5 so the 4 increases by 1. The answer is **£3.50**.

We are looking at the 2. This is less than 5. The answer is **£6.70**.

> **£2.80 + £3.50 + £6.70 = £13.00**
>
> The estimated total is £13.00.
> The actual total is £12.94.
> By using the nearest 10p instead of the nearest whole pound, the estimate was much closer to the actual value.

Remember! Because we are working with money we have to put a zero in the Hundredths column.

Negative numbers

Sometimes numbers are called negative. This is a bit confusing but we use negative numbers in everyday life without even realising it.

A negative number is *a number below zero.*

Why do I need to know this?
We use negative numbers in bank accounts but the most common use is in temperatures. We need to understand how numbers work when they are less than zero.

Two good examples of negative numbers you will come across are in **money** and **temperature**.

 Money

If someone has a bank account then the statements the bank send show how much money is in the account.

If the money spent is more than that available, the statement will show a negative number.

Black numbers show the account is in credit, which is another way of saying there is money still in the account.

Red numbers show that too much money has been taken out of the account. The customer owes this money to the bank.

These numbers have a minus sign in front of them to show that they are negative numbers.

Bank Statement

Account Activity

Date	Payment Details	Paid out (£)	Paid in (£)	Balance (£)
			£1,200	£1,200
19 Jun	Wages			£900
21 Jun	Shopping	£300		£450
21 Jun	Rent	£450		£385
25 Jun	Bills	£65		£485
25 Jun	Cash deposit		£100	-£115
28 Jun	Holiday	£600		

➡ Temperatures

Temperatures often use negative numbers.

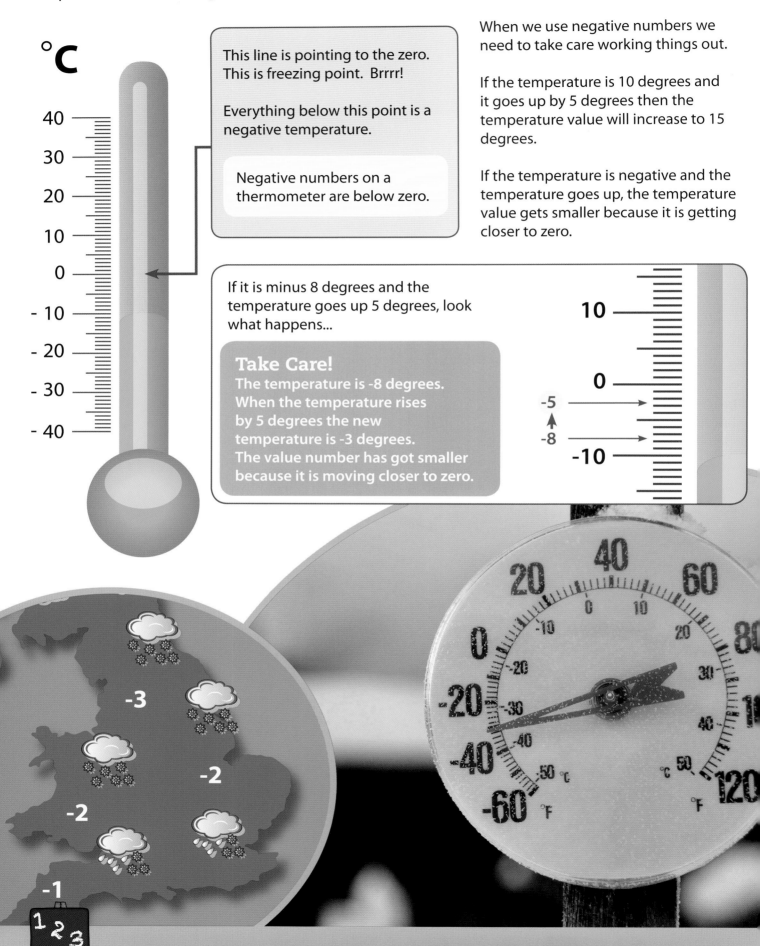

°C

40
30
20
10
0
- 10
- 20
- 30
- 40

This line is pointing to the zero. This is freezing point. Brrrr!

Everything below this point is a negative temperature.

Negative numbers on a thermometer are below zero.

When we use negative numbers we need to take care working things out.

If the temperature is 10 degrees and it goes up by 5 degrees then the temperature value will increase to 15 degrees.

If the temperature is negative and the temperature goes up, the temperature value gets smaller because it is getting closer to zero.

If it is minus 8 degrees and the temperature goes up 5 degrees, look what happens...

Take Care!
The temperature is -8 degrees. When the temperature rises by 5 degrees the new temperature is -3 degrees. The value number has got smaller because it is moving closer to zero.

10

0

-5

-8

-10

-3

-2

-2

-1

Ratios

Why do I need to know this?

We use ratios to work out how to dilute things such as screen wash, juice drinks and cleaning products. We also use them for working out how much of something we need to buy.

We use ratios more often than we might realise so we need to know how to work them out confidently.

We need to dilute squash at a ratio of 1 part squash to 5 parts water to make a drink.
The sum, or total, of the parts makes 1 whole quantity.

1:5 1 part squash to 5 parts water is written 1 : 5

Ratios are always written using the colon sign (:) to show that we are comparing the two values.
1 : 5 makes **6 parts in total**.
We need all 6 parts to make up one whole mixture.

Let's take a look at a few examples using ratios...

The following recipe for pancakes makes 8 small pancakes, enough for 1 very hungry person.
- 100 g Plain Flour
- 140 ml Milk
- 1 Egg

We can write this as a ratio of eggs to flour to milk.

Eggs	:	Flour	:	Milk
1	**:**	**100**	**:**	**140**

It doesn't matter that they are not the same measure or units because we only need to know how many 'parts' we need in one total batch or recipe mix.

In a class there is a ratio of 3 boys to 7 girls. To write this as a ratio we **use the colon sign**.

3:7 The ratio of boys to girls is 3 : 7.

Did you spot that the words are in the same order as the number values?

'Boys to girls' and '3 : 7'.

3:7 not **7:3**

We can't say the ratio of girls to boys is 3 : 7 or the ratio of boys to girls is 7 : 3 because they would both mean we had 3 girls and 7 boys, which is the wrong way round.

Remember! →

A Ratio is a way of comparing values that, added together, make the whole amount.
It is very important to write the numbers in the ratio in the same order as the words in the question.

Functional Skills **MATHEMATICS**

One more example...

A builder wants to order sand and cement. He knows he needs one 25 kg bag of cement and three 25 kg bags of sand to cover a path 1 m x 3 m.

3:1 The ratio of **sand to cement** is 3 : 1.

Always remember to write the numbers in the same order as the words.

The builder needs 4 bags in total.

We can also write the ratio using the weights in kilograms the builder needs for one mixture

75:25 He needs 100 Kg in total.

This ratio covers the path 1 m x 3 m.

➡ Making ratio values bigger or smaller

Sometimes we need to alter the ratio values because we need more or less of something.

For example, do you remember this recipe?

What do we do if we need to make enough pancakes **for two very hungry people** or if we only want to make **4 rather than 8**?

The following recipe for pancakes makes 8 small pancakes, enough for **1 very hungry person**.

- 100 g Plain Flour
- 140 ml Milk
- 1 Egg

For 2 very hungry people...
We need to double all the values.

100 g Plain Flour x 2	=	200 g Plain Flour
140 ml Milk x 2	=	280 ml Milk
1 Egg x 2	=	2 Eggs

Eggs : Flour : Milk

2 : 200 : 280

For 4 pancakes instead of 8...
We need to halve all the values.

100 g Plain Flour ÷ 2	=	50 g Plain Flour
140 ml Milk ÷ 2	=	70 ml Milk
1 Egg ÷ 2	=	½ egg

Eggs : Flour : Milk

1/2 : 50 : 70

The ratios are the same in both examples above.
All the values are increased or reduced by the same proportion.

 **Remember!**

Decimals

➜ Decimal point

To start let's look again at place values and see how to find the decimal point in any number.

If a number doesn't show any decimal places or a decimal point then it comes **after the unit**. That is because the decimal point is always there, but when we are not using it we don't write it down.

Maths is a bit lazy and likes to make things simple!

Let's have a look at some numbers to find their decimal points...

Decimal point place value

37.5	It is between the 7 and the 5.
2,365.9	It is between the 5 and the 9.
389.2	It is between the 9 and the 2.

...too easy!

What about 247?
Just look for the Unit. The decimal point comes after the Unit so it is 247 . 0

Actually you could add as many zeros as you wanted to after the decimal point and it wouldn't change the number, but two is a useful number because we use 2 decimal places in money.

So, let's check some more numbers and show their decimal points. We will put 2 decimal places, or zeros, after each decimal point.

Remember! ➜

The decimal point divides the whole numbers from the values that are less than 1.

Where to place the decimal point?

The unit has been **coloured** to help with the first three.

67 becomes 67.00
200 becomes 200.00
3, 097, 001 becomes 3,097,001.00
93, 010 becomes 93,010.00

The decimal point comes *after the number* every time.

Try 27.54 does this need to have a decimal point added?

Take Care!
If you can't see the decimal, never put it in the middle of the number. It always goes after the Unit.

Look again: it is 27.54 so the decimal point is already there, between the 7 and the 5.

→ Multiplying by 10 or 100

It is useful to know how to multiply and divide by 10 or 100 because it can help you to work things out more quickly.
You will also need to know how to do this when working with **percentages** and working out **discounts and offers**.

To understand how we multiply or divide by 10 or 100 we need to think about place value columns.

TH H T U

Each place value column can count up from 0 to 9. Whenever we reach a value of Ten in a column we start using a larger place value column.

We can think of the way we count as being in 'bundles' of Ten.

When we count in the Units column we can count up to 9, but when we have a 'bundle of Ten' we put a 1 in the Tens column. This shows we have one 'bundle of Ten'.

In the Tens column the same thing happens: we have up to 9 'bundles of Ten' but when we reach the tenth bundle we put a '1' in the Hundreds column, to show we have collected 10 'bundles' of Ten.
10 bundles of Ten is the same as 100.

10 X 10 = 100

So we can say we have collected 10 'bundles of Ten' but as maths likes to keep things simple, we call it one 'bundle of a Hundred'.

In the Hundreds column we can collect 9 'bundles of 100' and when we reach the tenth bundle we have to put a 1 in the Thousands column.

So each place value column is **Ten Times Bigger** than the one before it.
This is useful when we want to multiply or divide by 10 or 100.

Now we know about place value columns and finding the decimal point let's do some multiplying by 10...

You borrow 2 books from the library each week for 10 weeks. How many books have you borrowed in total?

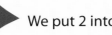 We put 2 into the units place value column.

We will put the decimal point in. We don't really need to use it in this sum but we want to get into a good habit and it will help us later on.

```
T  U
   2 . 0  0
```

Now multiply 2 by 10
$2 \times 10 = 20$

```
T  U
2  0 . 0  0
```

We can see that by multiplying 2 by 10 the 2 has moved into the Tens column.
The decimal point has not moved: it still comes after the Units column.

You get paid £3.00 a week for ten weeks. How much have you been paid?

We put the 3 into the Units column.

This time we need the decimal point because we are working with money and the places after the decimal point are for the pence.

```
 T  U
£ 3 . 0  0
```

We multiply the 3 by 10
$3 \times 10 = 30$

```
 T  U
£3 0 . 0  0
```

10 contains *one* zero; *one* zero has been used in the answer and the 3 has moved *one* place value column.
The decimal point has not moved.

This time we'll try multiplying by 100...

There are 25 biscuits in a packet. If the factory makes 100 packets an hour how many biscuits an hour do they make?

First think about the place value columns. Then add the decimal point.

```
H  T  U
   2  5 . 0  0
```

Now we are ready to multiply 25 by 100.
$25 \times 100 = 2500$

We will write the answer into the place value columns to see what has happened. We need to add another place value column so, just put the Thousands column on. No special permission is needed!

100 contains *two* zeros; we have used *two* zeros in the answer and the number 25 has moved *two* place value columns to the left.
The decimal point has not moved.

```
Th H  T  U
2  5  0  0 . 0  0
```

Functional Skills **MATHEMATICS**

This looks like a rule we can use...

Remember! →
- When you are multiplying a number ending in one or more zeros (10 or 100) count the zeros in that number.
- Move any digits across into larger place value columns by the same number of places as the number of zeros.
- *Multiplying numbers makes them bigger*.

Hang on, what if there are zeros in both numbers?

40 x 100

Place values first and decimal point next. We always need to be sure of where it is even if we are not using it yet.

```
H  T  U
   4  0  .  0  0
```

Now count the zeros in the sum. There are 3, but **be careful**. We only need to count the two zeros in the 100.
This is because we are already using the zero in the 40 in our sum and **we can't use it twice**.

We can **only count zeros we haven't written into the place value columns**; otherwise we will get the wrong answer.

```
Th  H  T  U
 4  0  0  0  .  0  0
```

In Functional Skills you would lose a mark if you counted three zeros because you would not be showing that you understand what you are doing.

The answer is 4,000.

→ Advanced method (multiplying by 10 or 100)

When you are more confident multiplying with 10 and 100 you can try using this method.
In the advanced method any zero is ignored and added in at the end.

25 x 100

We ignore the zeros and use 25 x 1 = 25.
Now we count the zeros in the original sum.
Add two zeros after the 25.

The answer is 2500.

1000 x 2300 x 20000

Ignore all the zeros: 1 x 23 x 2 = 46

Now count up all the zeros in the original sum. There are 9 zeros to write onto our answer. 46000000000.

The answer is 46,000,000,000.

 **Remember!**

A comma is put into a long number, counting every 3 places from the Units column. This makes it easier to read.

➡ Dividing by 10 or 100

Now that we are experts in place value columns and finding the decimal point, dividing should be a piece of cake!

Ten friends come to visit. You have 25 biscuits in the biscuit tin. How many biscuits is that each?

Place value columns first. This time we are dividing the number 25.

```
T  U   1/10  1/100
2  5 .  0    0
```

Next, add the decimal point. This is essential for dividing; we can't divide without it. ***Don't forget to add the zeros after the decimal point.***

We are dividing 25 by 10.
25÷10 = 2.5

Write the answer into the place value columns. Write it underneath the 25. **Line up the decimal points.**

```
T  U   1/10  1/100
2  5 .  0    0
   2 .  5    0
```

> This time the number has moved one place to the right.
> We had **one** zero in the Ten and the number has moved **one** place value column to the right.
> **The decimal point has not moved.**

So what are these place value columns on the right?

On the **left side** of the decimal point we have **whole numbers** with each place value column being 10 times larger than the one before.

On the **right side** of the decimal point we have **fractions of 1** with each place value being 10 times smaller than the one before.

We look more closely at working with decimals in the Decimals section of the book.

```
H  T  U  1/10  1/100
         0 .  1    0
```

So 2.5 in our answer above means 2 whole biscuits and 5/10 of a biscuit.

5/10 is the same as ½ so **the answer is 2½ biscuits each**.

Now let's try one using 100...

Tom saved £475. He buys 100 pairs of socks to sell on eBay, how much does each pair cost?

Place value columns first, then the decimal point.

```
 H  T  U
£4  7  5 . 0  0
```

Now work out 475 ÷ 100 = 4.75
Write the answer in underneath the 475.

```
 H  T  U   1/10  1/100
£4  7  5 .  0    0
£      4 .  7    5
```

This time we divided by 100. We had **two** zeros in the 100; the 475 moved **two** places to the right. *The decimal point has not moved.*

This looks like a rule we can use.

Remember! →

- When dividing by a number with one or more zeros count the zeros in that number.
- Move any digits across into smaller place value columns by the same number of places as the number of zeros.
- *Dividing numbers makes them smaller.*

Working with decimals

We have looked at addition, subtraction, multiplication and division of whole numbers already.
We have also found out how to multiply and divide by 10 or 100 using decimal places when number values are less than 1.

Now we will work out how to add, subtract, multiply and divide decimal numbers up to 2 decimal places.

When we say 2 **decimal places**, mathematicians think that takes a very long time to write, so we say 2 **dp** to make it easier for ourselves.

➡ Addition

When we do calculations in decimals we must always be careful to know where the decimal point is.

23.7 is a very different number to 2.37 or 237.00

Just remember that the decimal point **separates the whole numbers from the fractions** or bits of the number that are less than 1.

Let's try some addition sums

26.50 + 14.57

Always start any calculations by writing the sum out again in a way we can work with.

Never try and work it out without writing it out properly.

```
   T   U   1/10  1/100
   2   6 .  5    0
+  1   4 .  7    5
```

Remember to put the sign in.

Now add as usual, but instead of starting with the Units column we start with the **smallest place value**.
Each place value after the decimal point is smaller than the one on the left.
That is just the same as for the place value columns in the whole numbers before the decimal point.

Addition with decimals

So, 5 + 0 = 5
We can write that in under the answer line.

```
      T   U  1/10  1/100
      2   6 .  5    0
  +   1   4 .  7    5
      _____
                     5
```

Then we do the next column to the left, the 1/10 column.
5 + 7 = 12
That's too many for any of the place value columns as we can only go up to 9.

Remember! →

We learned with whole numbers that we can write in the 2 Units and carry the 1 Ten across to the next column.
The decimal point doesn't change that: we do exactly the same whether there is a decimal point there or not.

BUT we must write the decimal point into our answer; it goes in line with the decimal points in the sum. **It does not move**.

```
      T   U  1/10  1/100
      2   6 .  5    0
  +   1   4 .  7    5
      _____
              .  2    5
              1
```

Next the Units column. 6 + 4 + 1 = 11
Write in the 1 Unit and carry the 1 Ten across.

```
      T   U  1/10  1/100
      2   6 .  5    0
  +   1   4 .  7    5
      _____
          1 .  2    5
      1       1
```

Now the Tens column 2+1+1 = 4

```
      T   U  1/10  1/100
      2   6 .  5    0
  +   1   4 .  7    5
      _____
      4   1 .  2    5
      1       1
```

The answer is 41.25

Let's try another example using more numbers...

Addition with decimals

Here is a list of prices for a shopping basket.

Apples   £1.50
Bananas   £1.25
Bread   £1.00
Milk   £1.50
Jam   £1.25

We can add these amounts up in a sum using our place value columns.

```
T   U  1/10  1/100
    1 .  5    0
    1 .  2    5
    1 .  0    0
    1 .  5    0
+   1 .  2    5
  _____
```

```
T   U  1/10  1/100
    1 .  5    0
    1 .  2    5
    1 .  0    0
    1 .  5    0
+   1 .  2    5
  _____
              0
              1
```

Start with the smallest place value which is always the one on the right-hand side.

$0 + 5 + 0 + 0 + 5 = 10$

Write the zero from the 10 into the Units column, to show we have no units at the moment, and carry the 1 Ten across.

```
T   U  1/10  1/100
    1 .  5    0
    1 .  2    5
    1 .  0    0
    1 .  5    0
+   1 .  2    5
  _____
         5    0
         1    1
```

Now the next column

$5 + 2 + 0 + 5 + 2 = 14 + 1$ *(carried across)* $= 15$

Write the answer in and carry the Ten across. Don't forget to write the decimal point in. **_Keep it in line with the ones above_**.

```
T   U  1/10  1/100
    1 .  5    0
    1 .  2    5
    1 .  0    0
    1 .  5    0
+   1 .  2    5
  _____
    6    5    0
         1    1
```

Finally, add the Units column and write in the answer.

Remember this is money so you must show the £ sign.

The answer is £6.50.

Take Care!
Money always has two decimal places even when they are zeros.

Another way of adding this up is to see if you can find **number bonds**.

> 0.50 is the same as ½ so if you can see two 0.50 values you know you have made a whole 1.

> 0.25 is the same as ¼ so two 0.25 values will make ½ and 4 will make a whole 1.

```
  T   U   1/10  1/100
      1 . 5    0
      1 . 2    5
      1 . 0    0
      1 . 5    0
+     1 . 2    5
```

We can quickly see we have enough fractions to make up one whole 1 with the **two 0.50 values** and one half with the **two 0.25 values**.

We could write in the .50 and carry our one across in one calculation.

You could use your pen to tick number bonds so that you can group them together and count them up more easily.

Real mathematicians love any chance to write more things down!

➡ Subtraction

Subtracting decimals is exactly like subtracting whole numbers.

We just have to be careful that we always line up our decimal points. Let's try two different ones.

23.50 - 12.20

Always start by writing the sum in a way we can work with. Subtracting always has the **biggest number at the top**.

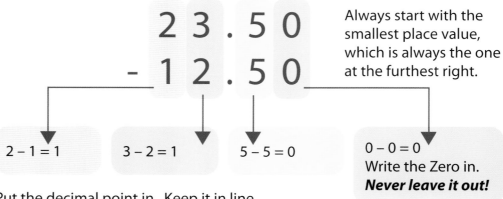

$$2 3 . 5 0$$
$$- 1 2 . 5 0$$

Always start with the smallest place value, which is always the one at the furthest right.

2 − 1 = 1   3 − 2 = 1   5 − 5 = 0   0 − 0 = 0
Write the Zero in. **Never leave it out!**

Put the decimal point in. Keep it in line. Work neatly.

```
    2 3 . 5 0
-   1 2 . 5 0
    ───────────
    1 1 . 0 0
```
The answer is 11.00

Only at the end can we decide to leave the zeros off and say the answer is 11.

19 - 2.30

Where is the decimal point in the 19?

We must put the decimal point in.
If we can't see one already then it **_always comes after the Unit_**.
We need to write in 2 zeros into the decimal places so we can line the numbers up properly.
Zeros are always there but we don't always need to write them in.

```
  1 9 . 0 0
-     2 . 3 0
  _____
```

Start with the right hand place value
0 - 0 = 0   Remember to write the zero in
0 - 3 =   Eeek! We can't do that yet.

Remember what happened with the whole numbers: we **borrowed** from the next place value on the left.

We don't need to worry about the decimal point being in-between as the decimal point is just to show us when we go from whole numbers to numbers that are less than 1.

```
  1 8⁹9̸ . ¹0 0
-       2 . 3 0
  _____
              0
```

Cross out the 9 to borrow Ten and write it into the Units column.

Now we can do
10 - 3 = 7
8 - 2 = 6
1 - 0 = 1

There is nothing to take away from the 1.

```
  1 8⁹9̸ . ¹0 0
-       2 . 3 0
  _____
    1 6 . 7 0
```

The answer is 16.70 to 2 dp.

➡ Multiplication

Multiplying decimals works best with the Lattice method or the Long Multiplication method. The Grid method is very complicated if there are decimal places in the sum.

We will do a sum and show it with the Lattice and Long Multiplication methods.

15.4 x 3.2

The first number has 3 digits and the second number has 2 digits so we need a lattice that is 3 squares by 2 squares.

Write the numbers across the top and right hand side as normal.

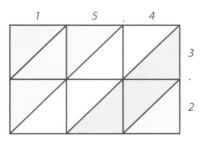

Notice the decimal points have been put in on the lines between the boxes.

Then continue with the multiplication just as in whole numbers.

On the top line
3 x 4
3 x 5
3 x 1

On the bottom line
2 x 4
2 x 5
2 x 1

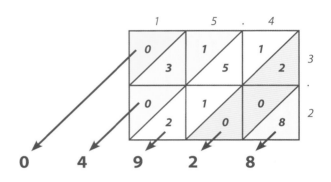

Add up the totals along the diagonals *ignoring the decimal points*.

Now we must work out *where to put the decimal point*.

We can **draw lines** from each decimal outside the boxes. Then follow the line down from where they meet to show the position of the decimal point.

This is shown with the blue arrows on the diagram (to the right).

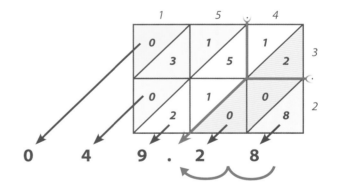

The other method is to **add the decimal places** after the decimal point **in the original sum** (15.4 x 3.2). There is 1 in the first number and 1 in the second number giving a total of 2 decimal places used.
This means there should be 2 decimal places in the answer.
Count in 2 places from the right to find the decimal point.

The answer is 49.28

Long Multiplication Method
Multiplying with decimals

Let's try the same sum using the long-multiplication method.

15.4 x 3.2

First we write the sum out in place value columns ready to work it out.

```
  1 5 . 4
x   3 . 2
```

While we are working out the sum we *ignore the decimal point completely.*

Just as in our whole number long multiplication we start with the right-hand place value in the bottom number and multiply it with each of the numbers in the top line.

2 x 4 = 8   2 x 5 =10   2 x 1 = 2
                    (carry the 1)   (add the carried 1 = 3)

```
  1 5 . 4            1 5 . 4            1 5 . 4
x   3 . 2      →   x   3 . 2     →    x   3 . 2
      8              0 8              3 0 8
                      1                  1
```

Now multiply the top line by the 3.
Don't forget to put a zero in the first place value column before you start.

3 x 4 = 12   3 x 5 = 15   3 x 1 = 3
(carry the 1)   (add the carried 1 = 16)   (add the carried 1 = 4)

```
  1 5 . 4            1 5 . 4            1 5 . 4
x   3 . 2      →   x   3 . 2     →    x   3 . 2
  3 0 8             3 0 8             3 0 8
  2 0               6 2 0            4 6 2 0
  1                 1   1             1   1
```

```
  1 5 . 4
x   3 . 2
  3 0 8
+ 4 6 2 0
  4 9 2 8
```

Now add up the two answers
to get the final total.

Now we have to find the correct place for the decimal point.
Count how many places in the original sum that came after the decimal.
15.4 has one place and 3.2 has one place. That is two places in total.

We must have two decimal places in our answer so the decimal point goes in after the 9.

The answer is 49.28.

➡ Dividing

When we divide a decimal number we ignore the decimal point while we are working the sum out.
We write the sum out just as we normally would for a whole number.

Short Division
with decimals

This example uses short division. **19.8 ÷ 6**

$$6\overline{)19.8}$$

$1 \div 6$

$19 \div 6 = 3r1$

$18 \div 6 = 3$

This can't be done so we carry it across to use the 9.
Write in the 3 and carry the remainder across to the next number.

$$\begin{array}{r} 3\,.\,3 \\ 6\overline{)1\ 9\,.^1 8} \end{array}$$

Write the answers in neatly and keep the decimal points in line.

Chunking
dividing
with decimals

This example uses chunking. **129.6 ÷ 4**

$$4\overline{)129.6}$$

$4 \times 10 = 40$

$4 \times 20 = 80$

$4 \times 30 = \boldsymbol{120}$ ⬅ 120 is a little bit less than 129.6

$4 \times 40 = 160$ ⬅ 160 is more than 129.6

The decimal point is after the Unit in 120.

$$\begin{array}{r} 4\overline{)129.6} \\ -120.0 \\ \hline 9.6 \end{array}$$ 4 x 30

$4 \times 1 = 4$

$4 \times 2 = \boldsymbol{8}$ ⬅ 8 is less than 9.6

$4 \times 3 = 12$ ⬅ 12 is more than 9.6

The decimal point is after the 8.

$$\begin{array}{r} 4\overline{)129.6} \\ -120.0 \\ \hline 9.6 \\ -\ \ 8.0 \\ \hline 1.6 \end{array}$$ 4 x 30 4 x 2

4 will not divide into 1.6 because 1.6 is smaller than 4.
Just as in short division we carry the 1 across to the next column to make 16.

```
       _____
    4) 1 2 9 . 6
     - 1 2 0 . 0        4 x 30
       _____
         9 . 6
     -     8 . 0        4 x 2
       _____
         ✗ . ¹6
```

4 x 1 = 4
4 x 2 = 8
4 x 3 = 12
4 x 4 = **16** ⬅ This is the number we are looking for.
4 divides into 16 exactly 4 times.

```
         3 2 . 4
       _____
    4) 1 2 9 . 6
     - 1 2 0 . 0        4 x 30
       _____
         9 . 6
     -     8 . 0        4 x 2
       _____
         ✗ . ¹6
           . ¹6        4 x 4
       _____
             0
```

Take Care!
We are working *after* the decimal point here. This means we have to *put the answer after* the decimal point.

The answer is 32.4.

➡ Sorting decimals by size

We looked before at how to put whole numbers into size order by looking at their place values.

The same works for decimals.

The thing that sometimes confuses people is that when whole numbers get bigger they get more and more place value columns on the left of the decimal point.

9.0
99.0
999.0
9999.0
99999.0
999999.0
9999999.0

When more numbers are added on the right side of the decimal they get smaller and smaller.

Remember! ➡

All place value columns are ten times bigger than the one on their right.

0.2
0.02
0.002
0.0002
0.00002
0.000002
0.0000002

Ordering decimals. Start by lining up the decimal points...

	H	T	U	.	1/10	1/100	1/1000
0.325			0	.	3	2	5
12.872		1	2	.	8	7	2
127.091	1	2	7	.	0	9	1
6.001			6	.	0	0	1
1.010			1	.	0	1	0
38.976		3	8	.	9	7	6
101.014	1	0	1	.	0	1	4

Functional Skills **MATHEMATICS**

We can sort these into size order starting with the one with Hundreds in the place value at the top. Then the Tens only and then the Units only numbers.

```
1  2  7  .  0  9  1
1  0  1  .  0  1  4
   3  8  .  9  7  6
   1  2  .  8  7  2
      6  .  0  0  1
      1  .  0  1  0
      0  .  3  2  5
```

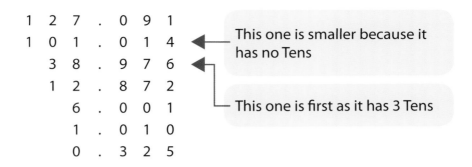

This one is smaller because it has no Tens

This one is first as it has 3 Tens

Let's try a few with just decimal places.

0.001
0.210
0.010
0.901
0.999
0.050
0.005
0.505

This looks tricky but remember:
Every place value is larger than the one on the right.

It is just the same as with whole numbers.

If we ignore the decimal place for now we want to find numbers with digits in the **_biggest column_**.

In this example, it is the Tenths column, the first one after the decimal point.

The nearer to the decimal point the place value column gets, the closer to a whole 1 it gets.

The far away columns are far away from being a whole 1.

**Ordering the
decimal places**

		1/10	1/100	1/1000	
0	.	9	9	9	This one has Tenths and Hundredths; this means it is bigger than the next number.
0	.	9	0	1	This starts with Tenths but has no Hundredths.
0	.	5	0	5	The next biggest number in the Tenths column is this one which starts with 5.
0	.	2	1	0	This is the last number with a digit in the Tenths column.
0	.	0	5	0	This number starts with the largest Hundredth.
0	.	0	1	0	This starts with the next largest Hundredth.
0	.	0	0	5	Now we only have numbers starting with Thousandths.
0	.	0	0	1	This number starts with the smallest Thousandth.

Using a formula

Don't panic!
You have probably seen sums or a formula with letters and sometimes symbols in instead of numbers.

They can look quite confusing, but in **Level 1 Functional Skills** you only need to use **formulae** (the word for more than one formula) **using words**.

Written formulae help you get used to working things out **using a rule**, and in **Level 2 Functional Skills** you will learn how to use that skill to work out **formulae with letters and symbols** as well.

Why do I need to know this?
Formulae are used in every day life, for example to work out times in different places, for diluting a mixture accurately, when buying sale items or working out the costs of a 'best offer'.

The **method for using a formula** is always the same: you need to find the number values to put into the formula and turn it into an ordinary sum with numbers.

Here is an example that works out time difference...

You have a friend in Australia who wants to phone you at 9 p.m. but **Australian time is 8 hours ahead of UK time**. What time will it be in Australia when it is 9 p.m. in the UK?

The formula is:

> **UK time + 8 hours = Australia time**

We need to use the time in the question to replace the 'UK time' in the formula.

> **9 p.m. + 8 hours = 5 a.m.**

This example works out a special offer...

You want to buy some shampoo and conditioner and the shop has a special offer advertised:

> 66 *Any 3 hair products for the price of 2.* 99
> *Cheapest one free.*
>
> | | | |
> |---|---|---|
> | **Shampoo** | **£1.50** | ← x2 |
> | Hair spray | £1.99 | |
> | **Conditioner** | **£1.25** | ← x1 |
> | Hair gel | £2.15 | |
> | Hair colour | £4.50 | |

In Functional Skills you will have to decide for yourself which products to choose. In this example we will choose **2 bottles of shampoo and 1 bottle of conditioner**.

The formula is telling us to find our 3 prices first and to **only add up the 2 most expensive ones**.

£1.50 + £1.50 + £1.25 ←——— Cheapest one.
£1.50 + £1.50 = £3.00

Fractions

➡ What is a fraction?

Fractions are parts of a whole one.
Every time we divide something into smaller equal parts we are making fractions.
When we put all the parts back together we make the whole one again.

Take a cake for example. If we are feeling generous we might want to share it with some friends.

Let's start with just one friend...

2 equal parts

To divide the cake into *2 equal parts* we need to cut it into two halves. These two halves together *make one whole* cake.

We write this as $\frac{1}{2}$

Now let's share the cake with 3 friends...

4 equal parts

This time we will need to divide the cake in to *4 equal parts*. We need to cut it into four quarters. These four quarters together *make one whole* cake.

We write this as $\frac{1}{4}$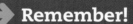

➡ Remember!

The top number shows us how many *equal parts* are for us.

The bottom number tells us how many *equal parts make* the *whole thing*.

The simple examples on the previous page show how fractions have a top and bottom number.

We name fractions by using the top number and then the bottom number.

So in these fractions we can see.

$\frac{2}{5}$ = two fifths   It means we actually have 2 parts and we need 5 parts to make one whole one up again.

$\frac{3}{10}$ = three tenths   It means we actually have 3 equal parts but we need 10 of them to make one whole again.

➡ Working with fractions

In Decimals we learned that the numbers to the right of the decimal point get smaller and smaller.
These are the numbers with a value of less than 1.
The place value columns sound bigger: Tenths, Hundredths, Thousandths, Ten Thousandths, etc,
but because they are **fractions of 1** they are really getting smaller and smaller.

Fractions are like this too.

The top number is called the **Numerator** but don't worry we will just call it the top number.
The bottom number is called the **Denominator**, and we will call it the bottom number.

When the top number is 1 we can see that the bigger the bottom number gets the smaller the fraction gets.

Splitting one whole into equal parts

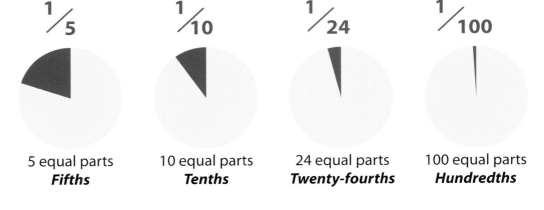

| $\frac{1}{5}$ | $\frac{1}{10}$ | $\frac{1}{24}$ | $\frac{1}{100}$ |

5 equal parts **Fifths**   10 equal parts **Tenths**   24 equal parts **Twenty-fourths**   100 equal parts **Hundredths**

This is because the **top number** is the number of parts we have (in this case just 1 part). The **bottom number** is the number of equal parts that the whole has been divided up into.

The bigger the bottom number the more equal parts we have made from our whole, so the smaller each part is.

If we divide our cake into 100 equal parts they will be very tiny slices indeed!

Large top numbers can be misleading

Look at these fractions:

Five tenths sounds smaller than one quarter because there are ten equal parts needed to make up one whole instead of four equal parts, but look at the diagram.

Because we have five tenths (5/10), that makes up a half of the parts needed to make up one whole. We only have one quarter (1/4) so it is actually the smaller of the two fractions.

If we want to sort these kinds of fractions we need to compare them more carefully. We can use a **fraction wall** to help us do this.

A fraction wall

One Whole									
1/2					1/2				
1/3			1/3			1/3			
1/4		1/4		1/4		1/4			
1/5	1/5		1/5		1/5		1/5		
1/8	1/8	1/8	1/8	1/8	1/8	1/8	1/8		
1/10	1/10	1/10	1/10	1/10	1/10	1/10	1/10	1/10	1/10

Let's put these fractions into size order using the fraction wall

$$\frac{1}{5} \quad \frac{2}{3} \quad \frac{3}{8} \quad \frac{4}{10} \quad \frac{3}{4}$$

Comparing fractions using a fraction wall

One Whole									
1/2					1/2				
1/3			1/3			1/3			
1/4		1/4		1/4		1/4			
1/5	1/5		1/5		1/5		1/5		
1/8	1/8	1/8	1/8	1/8	1/8	1/8	1/8		
1/10	1/10	1/10	1/10	1/10	1/10	1/10	1/10	1/10	1/10

From here it is easy to see which are the biggest and smallest fractions.

$$\frac{3}{4} \rightarrow \frac{2}{3} \rightarrow \frac{4}{10} \rightarrow \frac{3}{8} \rightarrow \frac{1}{5}$$

We can also use a fraction wall to see **equivalent fractions**; these are fractions that have the same value even though they look different.

One Whole		

1/3	1/3	1/3

1/6	1/6	1/6	1/6	1/6	1/6

One Whole			

1/4	1/4	1/4	1/4

1/8	1/8	1/8	1/8	1/8	1/8	1/8	1/8

One Whole				

1/5	1/5	1/5	1/5	1/5

1/10	1/10	1/10	1/10	1/10	1/10	1/10	1/10	1/10	1/10

Here is an example of where we need to use fractions...

A packet of sweets contains **20 toffees**. There are **4 children** who want to share the packet. How many toffees does each child get?

First let us work out what the fraction looks like.

We need to divide the whole amount into **4 equal parts**, one for each child. That is the **bottom number** (the number of equal parts that the whole amount is divided into).

We want to know what 1 child gets. That is the **top number** (one part).

$\frac{1}{4}$ Each child gets one quarter

We need to divide the 20 toffees into 4 equal parts to find a quarter of 20.

$$\begin{array}{r} 5 \\ 4\overline{)2\ 0} \end{array}$$ 5 toffees in each quarter, so that is **5 toffees for each child**.

Here is another example...

Custard powder is mixed using **2 tablespoons of powder** and **600 ml of milk**. This makes **enough for 8 people**. How much milk and powder would you need for 6 people?

First we need to work out what 6 people is as a fraction.

We had 8 people altogether sharing the full mixture, so **8 is the bottom number** (the number of equal parts that together make one whole mixture).

This time we actually only have 6 people, so that is our top number.

$$\frac{6}{8}$$

We can use the fraction wall to see what equivalent fractions there are.

Equivalent fractions in everyday life

One Whole							
1/2				1/2			
1/4		1/4		1/4		1/4	
1/8	1/8	1/8	1/8	1/8	1/8	1/8	1/8

$$\frac{6}{8}$$ **is the same as** $$\frac{3}{4}$$

Take Care!
If using this method to simplify a fraction, always divide **both numbers** by the same amount.

We could also have found this value by dividing both the top and bottom numbers in the fraction by 2.

We need $\frac{3}{4}$ of the recipe for custard for 6 people.

We need to **divide the total values by 4** (our bottom number) and add up the 3 parts we have; this is the same as **multiplying by 3**.

Here is a picture showing how the sugar has been divided into 4 equal parts to find 4 quarters.

We have then added 3 of the quarters together to find 3/4.

$\frac{3}{4}$ of 2 tablespoons is $1\frac{1}{2}$ tablespoons.

600 ml is divided by 4 to find one quarter part.

$1\frac{1}{2}$ **tablespoons of custard powder**

```
   150
4)600
```

150 ml is one quarter so we multiply by 3 quarter parts needed.
150 x 3 = 450 ml.

$\frac{3}{4}$ of 600 ml of milk is 450 ml.

450 ml of milk

Another way to find fractions is to do repeated division...

Another way...

For the 600 ml of milk, to find ¼ we could divide the 600 by 2, to give us ½ and then divide the answer by 2 to give us ¼.

Another example...

You are making two matching bed covers.
They use 3 ¼ metres of fabric each. The shop has a roll of fabric with 8 ½ metres left on it.
How much fabric will be left on the roll after your material has been cut off?

First add up the two
pieces of fabric you need.

$$3¼ + 3¼$$

$$3 + 3 = 6$$

$$¼ + ¼ = ½$$

$+$

Total fabric = **6½** metres

Now take that away from the 8 ½ metres the shop starts with.

$$8½ - 6½ = 2 \text{ metres}$$

Functional Skills **MATHEMATICS**

Simplifying fractions

➡ What does simplifying mean?

To make things easier we try to use fractions in their smallest or simplest form...

Let's look at these fractions. They all look very different.

$\dfrac{6}{8}$　　$\dfrac{18}{24}$　　$\dfrac{15}{20}$

If we have to add them up it looks like it will be too hard to do. That's where simplifying comes in to help!

Let's make some fractions bigger first to see how it works...

Multiplying to make fractions bigger...

$\dfrac{1}{2}$　　We can multiply the top and bottom number by 2.　　$\dfrac{1}{2} \times \dfrac{2}{2} = \dfrac{2}{4}$

$\dfrac{2}{4}$　　This has the same value as one half.
If we divide the top and bottom by 2 we get back to ½.

What about multiplying by 3?

$$\dfrac{1}{2} \times \dfrac{3}{3} = \dfrac{3}{6}$$

$\dfrac{3}{6}$　●　This still has the same value as one half.
If we divide the top and bottom by 3 we get back to ½.

We can see that when we multiply the **top and bottom** by the **same number** it doesn't change the value of the fraction.

> **Take Care!**
> You must **multiply both the top and bottom** numbers for this to work.

Now let's use this to simplify the fractions we had earlier.

$\dfrac{6}{8}$　　$\dfrac{18}{24}$　　$\dfrac{15}{20}$

Dividing fractions to simplify them.

⁶⁄₈

6 and 8 are both even numbers so divide the top and bottom numbers by 2.

$$\frac{6}{8} \div \frac{2}{2} = \boxed{\frac{3}{4}}$$

⁶⁄₈ **simplifies to** ³⁄₄

---

¹⁸⁄₂₄

We look for a number that can be divided into both the top and bottom numbers of the fraction.

Knowing your times tables will help you find these numbers more quickly.

2, 3 and 6 all divide into both 18 and 24. It doesn't matter which one you start with as long as you use the **same number to divide both the top and bottom** of the fraction.

Dividing twice

We will divide by 2...

$$\frac{18}{24} \div \frac{2}{2} = \frac{9}{12}$$

We can divide this again by 3...

$$\frac{9}{12} \div \frac{3}{3} = \boxed{\frac{3}{4}}$$

¹⁸⁄₂₄ **simplifies to** ³⁄₄

---

¹⁵⁄₂₀

One number in this fraction is odd so we can't divide by 2 to simplify it.

We need a number that can divide into both 15 and 20.

We can use 5.

$$\frac{15}{20} \div \frac{5}{5} = \boxed{\frac{3}{4}}$$

All the fractions have the same value in their simplest form (¾) so we can add them up much more easily.

Converting fractions and decimals

If we are adding up ¼, ½ and ¾ on a calculator we need to **convert the fractions into decimals** to enter them onto the calculator.

Why do I need to know this?

Fractions and decimals sometimes need converting. We need to understand this when dealing with money, when we use a calculator, when measuring lengths and in other situations.

➡ Decimals into fractions

Place value columns and decimal points.

```
U .  1/10  1/100
0 .  1    0
```
is the same as 10/100.

This simplifies to 1/10 when we divide by 10.

We will write some decimals and see what they are as fractions...

```
U .  1/10  1/100
0 .  2    0
```
is the same as 20/100.

...or 2/10 when we simplify by dividing by 10. This simplifies to **1/5** when we divide again by 2.

```
0 . 2   5
```
is the same as 25/100.

This simplifies to **1/4** if we repeatedly divide by 5 or once by 25.

```
0 . 5   0
```
is the same as 50/100 or 5/10.

This simplifies to **1/2** when we divide by 5.

```
0 . 7   5
```
is the same as 75/100.

This simplifies to **3/4** if we divide by 25.

➡ Fractions into decimals

We can also convert **fractions into decimals**. The easiest way is by using a calculator. Enter the top number and divide by the bigger bottom number.

 $\frac{3}{4}$ would be $3 \div 4 = 0.75$

Here is an example of using fractions and decimals when measuring...

Wood is sold in lengths of 1.2 m, 2.4 m or 3.6 m.

You are making a rabbit run and need four lengths at 1 ½ metres each.
Which lengths of wood should you buy?

First we need to convert the fractions into decimal lengths. $1\frac{1}{2} = 1.5$

1.5 x 4 = 6 m of wood

We can't get 1.5 m out of the shortest length of 1.2 m and we can only get 2 lengths out of each 3.6 m piece. So we need to buy four 2.4 m pieces or two 3.6 m pieces.

Two 3.6 metre lengths will leave us with the least amount of wasted wood.

Functional Skills **MATHEMATICS**

Percentages

Why do I need to know this?

We use percentages every day. We see them in **adverts**, **newspapers**, **written information** and **special offers**. We need to know how to change between fractions, percentages and decimals to help us at home and at work.

The Word 'Percent' comes from an old language called Latin. 'Per' is all about the part or fraction and 'Cent' is telling us that it is out of 100.
Think of <u>cent</u>ipedes with their 100 legs.

Remember!

Percentages are always out of 100, So 100% is the whole amount.

Percentages are easy to work out...

Remember the place value columns and the decimal point?

U . 1/10 1/100

What happened when we multiplied by 10 or 100?

The number increased by the same number of zeros and moved into the larger place value columns.

15 x 100 = 1500

Th	H	T	U	.	1/10	1/100
1	5	0	0			
		1	5			

2.5 x 10 = 25

T	U	.	1/10	1/100
2	5	.	0	
	2	.	5	

We can use this understanding to help us divide numbers to find 1% and 10%.

1% is the same as 0.01 or 1/100.
The whole value has been divided up into 100 equal parts and we have 1 of them.
1/100 has **two zeros** in so the number moves **two places**.

How to find 1% of 350

Think about where the decimal point is in the number 350.

Remember, if there is no decimal point, it comes after the last Unit.

So 350 is the same as writing 350.0

We normally leave the decimal point out when we are not using it because it's lazier.

When we **multiply** by 10 or 100, the number moves across into the **larger** place value columns by the same number of zeros.

When we **divide** by 10 or 100, the number moves across into the **smaller** place value columns by the same number of zeros.

To find 1% we must divide by 100

H	T	U	.	1/10	1/100
3	5	0	.	0	
		3	.	5	0

Move right to make it smaller

3.5 is 1% of 350.
3.5 is one hundredth of 350.

Functional Skills **MATHEMATICS**

Now let's find 10% of 45.

10% is the same as 0.1 or 10/100.
10/100 can be simplified to 1/10.

The whole value has been divided up into 100 equal parts and we have 10 of them.

When we find 10% we want to find 1/10 of the number.

1/10 has one zero in so the number will move one place.

```
T  U  .  1/10
4  5  .  0           →   Decimal point
   4  .  5               moves right to
                         make it smaller.
```

4.5 is 10% of 45.
4.5 is one tenth of 45.

What about a 20% off sale?

TV was 1,800, now with 20% off!

How much is the discount on this TV?

20% is 2 lots of 10%, so find 10% first and then double it.

When we find 10% the number moves one place to the right.

```
Th  H  T  U  .  1/10
1   8  0  0          →   Decimal point
    1  8  0  .  0        moves right to
                         make it smaller.
```

10% of £1,800 is £180.

Now double £180 to find 20%
180 x 2 = £360

The TV has £360 off.

To find the new cost we would subtract £360 from £1800 to give the new price.

£1,800 - £360 + £1,440.

Now we'll find a 10% increase.

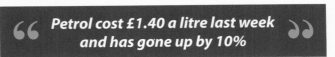
Petrol cost £1.40 a litre last week and has gone up by 10%

What is the new cost of a litre of petrol?

First find the 10% value.
£1.40 divided by 10 is £ 0.14

Now add the increase on to the original cost.
The increase is 14p so the new cost of a litre of petrol is £1.40 + 14p = **£1.54**

Another example to calculate pay rises.

Two people have a pay rise:
Fred earns £200 per week and gets a 10% rise.
Lucy earns £300 per week and gets a 5% rise.

Who gets the biggest pay rise?

Fred gets 10% of £200
- that is 10/100 or 1/10 giving him £20 extra.
Lucy gets 5% of £300
- that is 5/100 this simplifies to 1/20

There are three methods for finding 5% of £300. They are all correct and you can use whichever one you like best.

1) We can divide £300 by 20 to find 1/20.
```
      15
20)300
```

2) We can find 10% of £300 and halve it by dividing it by 2.
   £300 ÷ 10 = £30   £30 ÷ 2 = £15

3) We can find 1% of £300 and multiply by 5.
   £300 ÷ 100 = £3   £3 x 5 = £15

Fred gets £20 and Lucy gets £15.
Fred got double the percentage rate increase that Lucy got but we have to work out the percentage sums to find out the actual values.

Remember!

Sometimes we can use more than one method to make it easier.
We can find any percentage value by dividing by 100 to find 1% and multiplying by the number.

The most common percentage values at Level 1 Functional Skills will be:

5%   10%   20%   25%   50%   75%

If you have a look in the fractions and decimals section these percentage numbers may look familiar!

Rules for finding percentages

First find the decimal point
E.g. 325**.**5

If you can't see it already it will come after the last whole number.
E.g. 425 = 425**.**0

To find 10% the number in the sum moves one place value to the right.
E.g. 10% of 425.0 = 42.50

To find 1% the number moves two places to the right.
E.g. 1% of 325.5 = 3.255

Never change the order of the digits in your number.

 Converting to fractions and decimals

We need to look at what the percentage values look like when we write them as fractions and decimals.

% (Percentage)	Fraction	Simplified Fraction	Decimal
5%	5/100	1/20	0.05
10%	10/100	1/10	0.10 or 0.1
20%	20/100	1/5	0.20 or 0.2
25%	25/100	1/4	0.25
50%	50/100	1/2	0.50 or 0.5
75%	75/100	3/4	0.75

So now we know that 75% off in a sale is the same as ¾ off.
50% is the same as ½.
25% is the same as ¼.

Functional Skills **MATHEMATICS**

Using a calculator

➡ Entering calculations

Calculators can have many different functions on them and each make of calculator can be slightly different to use.

This section isn't going to explain exactly how every calculator works because that would be impossible!

We will look at how we can use calculators to work out **fractions, decimals** and **percentages**.

To calculate with a fraction we need to turn the fraction into a decimal value that the calculator can use.

> We already know ½ is the same as 0.5.
> We can **convert fractions into decimals by dividing the top number by the bottom number**.
> Enter 1÷2 into the calculator and press equals: the display shows 0.5.

Try some other fractions to see how easily the calculator converts fractions to decimals for us.

| $\frac{2}{3}$ = 2 ÷ 3 = 0.666 |
| $\frac{3}{4}$ = 3 ÷ 4 = 0.75 |
| $\frac{7}{28}$ = 7 ÷ 28 = 0.25 |

We can use the calculator to find percentages for us.

To find 15% of £350, enter...

[350] [×] [15] [%] [=]   52.5

To find what the new cost is when the 15% is taken off, enter...

[350] [−] [15] [%] [=]   297.50

John goes on a 48 km walk, but he stops after 36 km.

To find what percentage of the walk he managed to finish we need to find what 36 km is as a percentage of the total distance 48 km.

[36] [÷] [48] [%] [=]   75

Functional Skills **MATHEMATICS**

Recurring numbers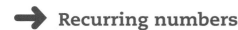

Sometimes calculators give answers like this: **3.666666666**   **456.777777**   **2.99999999**

These decimal places are called *recurring*. They happen because fractions can't always be written exactly into decimal numbers. We need to round these to make the numbers easier to work with.

Recurring decimal	Rounded to the nearest whole number	Rounded to 2 dp
3.666666666	4	3.67
456.777777	457	456.78
2.999999	3	3.00

> Have a look in the *Rounding* section if you need a bit more practice with rounding and decimal places.

Checking working out

> **Remember!** In Functional Skills checking working out is very important and gets some marks.

We can use the calculator to do a check on a sum we have written out in full.

This could be by doing a *repeat check* and using the calculator to do the same sum and check the answers are the same.

We could also do a *reverse check* by doing the calculation in reverse and seeing if we get the correct starting numbers.

Using a calculator for a reverse check

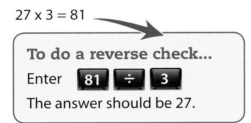

27 x 3 = 81

To do a reverse check...
Enter **81** ÷ **3**
The answer should be 27.

Take Care!
When we use a calculator it can be easy to make a mistake entering the numbers and using the other keys. The display answer might not be right.

Always look at the answer on the screen to see if it is about right.

You could use the repeat and reverse checks to see if the answer is correct or you could use approximation to estimate roughly what the answer should be.

> **Remember!** A calculator only uses the numbers you give it.
> If you give it the wrong instructions, it will give you the wrong answer!

Working with time

We use units of time every day:
Seconds to measure very short times and things that happen quickly.
Hours and **Minutes** to measure our day.
Days, **Weeks**, **Months** and **Years** to measure our lives.
A **Decade**, **Century** or **Millennium** to measure history.

Why do I need to know this?
We use time all the time!
We need to be able to read bus/train **timetables** easily, to **convert digital times** from a normal clock face and to help us **manage our time** better.

➡ Calculating with time

Time can be recorded on a clock face or on a digital clock.

12 hour clock...

On a **clock face**, and on some **digital displays**, the hours from 12 midnight to 12 midday and the hours from 12 midday to 12 midnight look the same whether it is morning or night.

Both clocks to the right show the time as 7.17, but when using a 12 hour clock you can't tell if it is morning or evening.

So we use A.M. for morning times before Midday and P.M. for afternoon times after Midday.

24 hour clock...

On a digital clock the hours can also be shown as a 24-hour display. This starts at 1 o'clock in the morning, 1 a.m., and continues until 24 hours have been completed. Midnight is shown as 00:00.

When the time reaches 1 o'clock in the afternoon the digital display just keeps counting, so 1p.m. is shown as 13:00. This is 12 hours, from midnight to midday, plus 1, 12+1=13.

60 Seconds = 1 Minute	
60 Minutes = 1 Hour	
24 Hours = 1 Day	
7 Days = 1 Week	
52 Weeks = 1 Year	
12 Months = 1 Year	
10 Years = 1 Decade	
100 Years = 1 Century	
1,000 Years = 1 Millennium	

Take Care!
Months can have 28, 29, 30 or 31 days in them.
There is between 4 and 4 ½ weeks in one month.

Functional Skills **MATHEMATICS**

Look at the clocks below to see how to work out some 24-hour times...

12 Midday plus 2 hours
12+2=14

This can also be written as:

2 o'clock
or
2 p.m.

12 Midday plus 7 ½ hours
12+7 ½=19 ½

There are 30 minutes in ½ hour.

This can also be written as:

Half past 7
or
7.30 p.m.

12 Midday plus 11 ¼ hours
12+11 ¼ =23 ¼

There are 15 minutes in ¼ hour.

This can also be written as:

Quarter past 11
or
11.15 p.m.

Let's try some examples using time...

Cooking a joint of meat

To cook a joint of meat the instructions say "30 minutes for every kilogram". The joint weighs 2.5 kg.

How long will it take to cook?

To work out how many minutes it will take in total we need to multiply the time given for 1 kg by the weight of the joint we are cooking.

2.5 x 30 = 75 minutes.

It takes 75 minutes, but we need to convert that to hours and minutes because that is how we normally measure time.

There are 60 minutes in 1 hour.
On a calculator you can divide 75 by 60 to get the answer 1.25.

Time on a calculator

> **Take Care!**
> Calculators do not show hours and minutes.
> They only show whole numbers and decimal fractions.

The answer, 1.25 hours, is the same as 1 ¼ hours or **1 hour and 15 minutes**. It is not 1 hour 25 minutes.

You are cooking a meal.
The joint of meat takes 1 ¼ hours to cook and fifteen minutes to serve.
You start cooking at 5 p.m.

What time will the meal be ready?

We need to add up all the times we need to include in our calculation.
1 ¼ hours for the cooking
15 minutes for serving

15 minutes is the same as ¼ hour.

1 ¼ + ¼ = 1 ½ hours.

Adding time

We need to add this on to our start time.

5 p.m. + 1 hour = 6 p.m.
6 p.m. + ½ hour = **6.30 p.m.**

One more example...

Jack records his working hours for a week.
Complete the record sheet to show how many hours he has worked in that week.

Day	Start	Finish	Hours worked
Monday	7.00 a.m.	4.00 p.m.	
Tuesday	6.30 a.m.	3.00 p.m.	
Wednesday	*Not working*		
Thursday	*Not working*		
Friday	6.00 a.m.	2.00 p.m.	

First count up the hours on each day and fill in the spaces on the record sheet.

Adding time to complete a time sheet

Monday 7 a.m. to 4 p.m.
Count on from 7 a.m. up to 12 midday.

7 8 9 10 11 12   That is 5 hours.

Now count on

7 8 9 10 11 12 1 2 3 4   That is 4 hours.

5 hours and 4 hours = **9 hours.**

Adding time to complete a time sheet

Tuesday 6.30 a.m. to 3 p.m.
First count on from 6.30 to the next whole hour.
That adds on 30 minutes or half an hour from 6.30 a.m. to 7 a.m..

Then count the hours up as before.

7 a.m. to 12 midday is 5 hours
12 midday to 3 p.m. is 3 hours

5 hours + 3 hours +½ an hour = **8 ½ hours.**

Friday 6.00 a.m. to 2 p.m.
6 a.m. to 12 midday is 6 hours
12 midday to 2 p.m. is 2 hours

6 hours + 2 hours = **8 hours.**
Now add up the total hours for the week.

9 + 8 ½ + 8 = **25 ½ hours.**

Reading timetables

Timetables can be used for journey times. They are also used for showing when TV programmes are on or what times films are on at the cinema.

We need to be able to read them to find out the information we need.

Times are normally written using hours and minutes. They do not show ¼ or ½, they show these in minutes as 15 or 30.

There are 60 minutes in 1 hour, so the times in minutes can be any value between 1 minute and 59 minutes.

Look at this bus timetable.

Service No.:	212	212	212	212	212	212	212	212	212	212
The Avenue	0510	0538	----	0610	0640	----	0702	----	----	0722
Town End	0512	0540	----	0612	0642	----	----	----	----	----
Town End	----	----	----	----	----	0652	----	0712	----	----
School Avenue	0514	0544	----	0614	0644	0656	0706	0716	----	0728
Town Hall arr.	0528	0558	----	0628	0658	0710	0720	0730	----	0745
Town Hall dep.	0532	0604	0624	0634	0704	0714	0724	0734	0743	0748
Broad Moor	----	----	0634	----	----	----	----	----	----	----
Broad Moor	0542	0614	----	0644	0714	0726	0736	0746	0756	0801
Grain Lane	0546	0618	----	0648	0718	----	0739	----	0800	----
Shopping Centre	----	----	----	----	----	0729	----	0749	----	0804

You catch the bus from School Avenue; it takes 10 minutes to walk to the bus stop. You have to be at the shopping centre for work by a quarter to 8.
What bus do you need to catch and what time do you have to leave home?

We need to work backwards to work this out.

First we need to look at the arrival times at the Shopping Centre to see which bus arrives on time.

You have to be at work by a quarter to 8. A quarter to 8 is 7.45.

08.04   arrives too late (after 7.45).
07.49   arrives too late (after 7.45).
07.29   this bus arrives before the start time for work.

Next follow the column above the 07.29 bus to see what time it leaves School Avenue.

Service No.:	212	212	212	212	212	212	212	212	212	212
The Avenue	0510	0538	----	0610	0640	----	0702	----	----	0722
Town End	0512	0540	----	0612	0642	----	----	----	----	----
Town End	----	----	----	----	----	0652	----	0712	----	----
School Avenue	0514	0544	----	0614	0644	*0656*	0706	0716	----	0728
Town Hall arr.	0528	0558	----	0628	0658	0710	0720	0730	----	0745
Town Hall dep.	0532	0604	0624	0634	0704	0714	0724	0734	0743	0748
Broad Moor	----	----	0634	----	----	----	----	----	----	----
Broad Moor	0542	0614	----	0644	0714	0726	0736	0746	0756	0801
Grain Lane	0546	0618	----	0648	0718	----	0739	----	0800	----
Shopping Centre	----	----	----	----	----	0729	----	0749	----	0804

It leaves School Avenue at 06.56.

It takes 10 minutes to walk from home to the bus stop.
We need to take 10 minutes away from 06.56 to work out what time we have to leave home

Just working with the minutes the sum is
56 - 10 = 46.

We need to leave home at 06.45

Take Care!
In Functional Skills make sure you have answered all the different parts of the question. Each part is worth marks.

Measuring things and converting units

Why do I need to know this?

We use many measures in everyday life.
Packets and tins come in weights; liquids we use, or dilute to use, come in volumes.
We measure our health and the weather with temperature.
We measure the things around us and ourselves using metres, centimetres and millimetres.

 Length and distance

We measure lengths using the **Metric** system.
This uses Millimetres, Centimetres, Decimetres and Metres. We usually measure longer distances in Metres and Kilometres.

The ruler below is measuring in millimetres (mm) and centimetres (cm).
10 millimetres make 1 centimetre.

| 1 Metre = 10 Decimetres |
| 1 Metre = 100 Centimetres |
| 1 Metre = 1000 Millimetres |
| 1,000 Metres = 1 Kilometre |

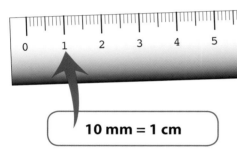

10 mm = 1 cm

In the past, lengths were measured using the **Imperial** system.
This uses inches, feet and yards.

Inches are longer than centimetres
2.54 cm is approximately 1 inch.

1 yard is a little bit less than 1 metre.
1 metre = approximately 39 inches.

When we measure longer distances we use Kilometres and we also use Miles from the Imperial system.

1 Kilometre is approximately 0.6 mile.

What is this arrow pointing to on the ruler?

The arrow is pointing between the 9 and the 10. It is over 90 mm or 9 cm.

Next count the smaller millimetre division lines. The arrow is pointing to the middle line. This is half a centimetre, which is 5 millimetres.

The arrow is pointing at 9.5 cm or 95 mm.

| 12 Inches = 1 Foot |
| 3 Feet = 1 Yard |
| 1 km = 1,000 Metres |
| 1 Mile = 1.6 km |

Functional Skills **MATHEMATICS**

What speeds are these dials showing?
Look at where the red line is pointing to.

Remember! → All measured units use a scale.
This is the interval or gap used between each of the lines on the dial or measuring tool.
Each scale can be different.

The first one is pointing to 60. Check what units we are using. It says miles/hr.
This is miles per hour so we can write that using the initial letters **60 mph**.

Take Care!
Always check you are using the correct units.

The next one is between two numbers.
We need to look at what the two numbers are so we can check the scale.

The numbers go up in 'tens'.
Tens have a bigger line and the smaller line is half-way between.
The smaller line shows 'fives'.
As you count each line around the dial you have to count up in fives.
The line is in the middle so it is showing **75 mph**, halfway between 70 and 80.

The third dial is also pointing between two numbers: 140 and 160.
On this dial the scale is different. The numbers go up in twenties but the biggest markers still show increases in tens.
The line is in the middle of 140 and 160, pointing at 150.
There are halfway lines on this dial too, showing 'fives'.
The dial is measuring in km/hr so it shows **150 km/hr**.

On the last dial the line is pointing at one of the smaller lines.
We worked out that these marked halfway between every ten.
It is past the 20, but has not reached the 30 mark.
So it is showing **25 km/hr**.

Distances are often worked out from a map.
The map below shows the distances between places on a route.
We have to add them up to find the total distance for a journey.

Look at this map and work out the distance from Dronfield to Huddersfax.

The map shows the distance between two red dots.

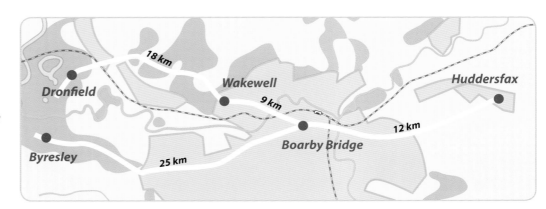

Functional Skills **MATHEMATICS**

We add up all the marked distances to find the total journey.
Dronfield to Wakewell = 18 km.
Wakewell to Boarby Bridge = 9 km.
Boarby Bridge to Huddersfax = 12 km.

$$18 + 9 + 12 = 39 \text{ km}$$

→ Weight

We weigh things in Grams and Kilograms.

In the old **Imperial** system things were weighed in Pounds (lb) and Ounces (oz). Many people still use these units too so we need to know about them.

1,000 g = 1 kg

16 oz = 1 lb

100 g = approximately 3.5 oz

1 kg = approximately 2 lb 3 oz

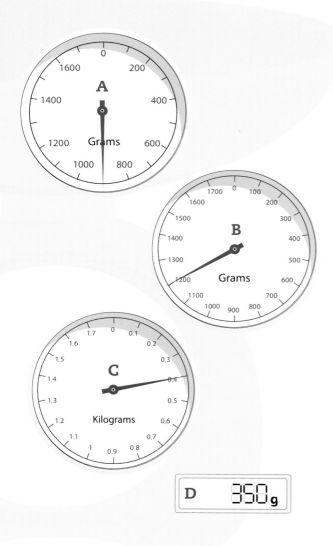

The dials on the left of this page show weights in grams and kilograms.

The first dial (A) is measuring in Grams.
The scale marker lines are shown every 100 g.
The needle is pointing between the 800 g and the 1000 g markers.
The first weight is **900 g**
There are 1,000 g in 1 kg so 900 g can also be written as **0.9 kg**.

U	.	1/10	1/100	1/1000	
1	.	0	0	0	1 kg = 1,000 g

U	.	1/10	1/100	1/1000	
0	.	9	0	0	900 g = 0.9 kg

The second dial (B) is measuring in Grams.
The needle is pointing at the **1200 g** marker line.
1200 g can also be written as **1.2 kg**.

The third dial (C) is measuring in Kilograms.
The scale marker lines are shown every 0.1 kg.
The needle is pointing at **0.4 kg**.
This can also be written as **400 g**.

The last scale (D) has a digital display.
We can just read the amount from the display.
This is **350 g**.
This can also be written as **0.35 kg**.

Remember! → We don't need a zero after the last digit unless we are using a set number of decimal places.

Liquid

Liquids can be measured using different units:
- In the **Metric** system liquids are measured in millilitres, centilitres and litres.
- In the **Imperial** system liquids are measured using pints.

1 Litre = 100 Centilitres	
1 Litre = 1,000 Millilitres	
1 Pint = 0.57 Litres (approx)	
1 Litre = 1¾ Pints (approx)	

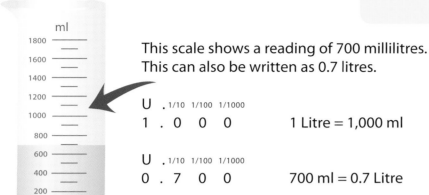

This scale shows a reading of 700 millilitres.
This can also be written as 0.7 litres.

U	.	1/10	1/100	1/1000	
1	.	0	0	0	1 Litre = 1,000 ml

U	.	1/10	1/100	1/1000	
0	.	7	0	0	700 ml = 0.7 Litre

Take Care! Confusing Maths Alert!
We measure liquids in litres (l), centilitres (cl) and millilitres(ml).
We often call them a volume...

But... in Maths, just to be confusing, we also call volumes of liquid **'units of capacity'**.
Litres, centilitres, millilitres are all units of capacity.

Capacity measures the amount of liquid volume a container can hold.
Volume is what we call the measure of any 3-D space and the unit we use is cubic (e.g. cm³ or m³).

Useful conversions to know:

1 litre =	**1 kg** =	**1,000 cm³** =	**0.001 m³**

1,000 litres =	**1 metric ton (1,000 kg)** =	**1 m³**

Temperature

There is something we measure that we can't actually pick up or see!

It is temperature.

Temperature is usually measured in Centigrade (C); this is sometimes called Celsius.
It can be measured in Fahrenheit (F) too.

After the number we write °C or °F.
The 'C' or 'F' show us which units we are using to measure the temperature. The little zero is maths shorthand for 'degree'.
Just as in a formula, it is a symbol to save us having to write out everything in words.

Maths is full of shorthand words and symbols - it is a bit like 'TXT SPK'.

100°C = 212°F	**0°C = 32°F**
This is boiling point for water.	*This is freezing point for water.*

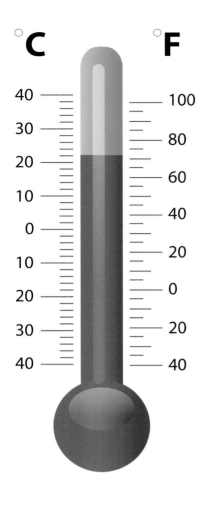

What is the temperature on this thermometer?

The top of the red liquid is where the temperature is shown.
Check the scale marker lines carefully.

On the Centigrade side the long marker lines are shown every ten degrees.
The smaller marker lines are shown every 2 degrees.
Count them up from zero to 10 degrees to check.
The Centigrade reading is **22°C.**

On the Fahrenheit side the long marker lines are shown every 20 degrees.
The medium length marker lines are shown to mark the 10 degrees between each of the number readings.
The shortest marker lines show every 5 degrees and come halfway between each of the medium length lines.
The red line is between the 70 and 75. It is showing a reading of about **72.5°F**.

Take Care!
It is very easy to make a mistake on a question with scales and dials to read.
Make sure you take time to work out what the scale is and what values the marker lines are showing you before you try to answer the question.

Shapes

Why do I need to know this?

We use the names of shapes in explaining and describing things, for example, a floor plan.
We need to know what shapes fit together, for example, when buying carpet for a room that is L-shaped, or for working out how many tiles we need to cover a wall.

➡ Regular shapes

We will look at some common regular shapes and what we need to know about them.

A **Regular Shape** is any shape where the sides are all the same length and the angles are all the same size.

Remember! ➡

Degrees are divisions of a circle.

There are 360 degrees in a circle.
There are 90 degrees in a right-angled corner.

We still use the ° symbol to save us writing out the word degrees every time.

Square

Four sides of equal length.
Four right-angle corners.

A right-angle has 90 degrees (90°).
We can fit 4 right-angles together with no gaps.

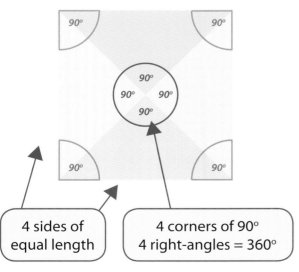

90°   90°

90°
90°   90°
90°

90°   90°

| 4 sides of equal length |
| 4 corners of 90° |
| 4 right-angles = 360° |

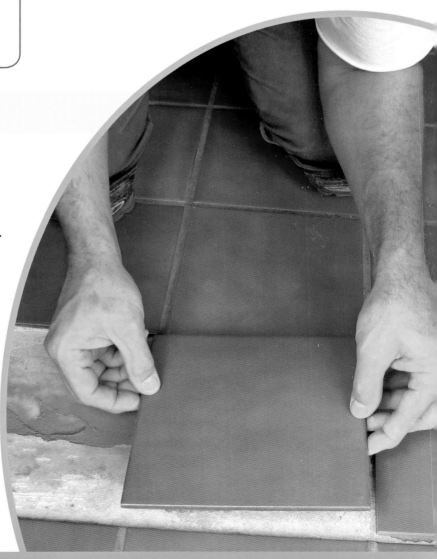

Triangle

A regular triangle has three equal sides.

All the angles added up make 180 degrees.

Only some triangles are regular.
Many are not regular.

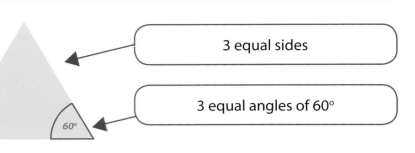

3 equal sides

3 equal angles of 60°

60°

Pentagon

A regular pentagon is a shape with five equal sides and 5 equal angles.

All the angles added up 540 degrees.

Not all pentagons are regular but their angles always add up to a total of 540°.

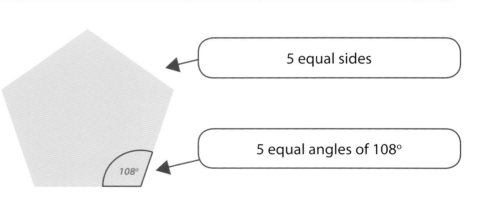

5 equal sides

5 equal angles of 108°

108°

Hexagon

A regular hexagon is a shape with 6 equal sides and 6 equal angles.

All the angles added together equal 720 degrees.

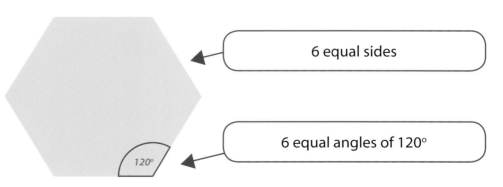

6 equal sides

6 equal angles of 120°

120°

Not all hexagons are regular. Any 6-sided closed shape is called a hexagon.

Functional Skills **MATHEMATICS**

→ Tessellating shapes

We will see which shapes tessellate...
Some regular shapes tessellate.

Tessellate is when shapes fit together without any gaps.

Squares

Squares tessellate. Think of these examples of squares which can tessellate.
- Tiles
- Boxes
- Garden paving slabs

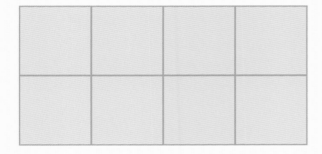

These tiles can fit together without any gaps between them.

Triangles

Regular triangles can tessellate.
Can you think of any regular triangles and how they tessellate?

Mmm, triangular chocolate bars...

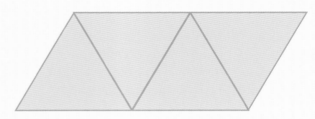

We have to rotate some of the triangles to make them fit together with no gaps.
That doesn't matter as long as there are no gaps.

Pentagons

Pentagons do not tessellate.

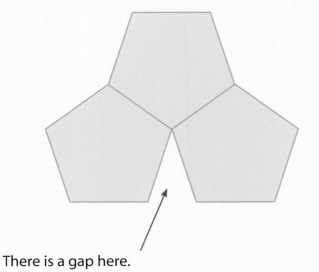

There is a gap here.

Hexagons

Hexagons tessellate and are often used for things like decorative tiles.

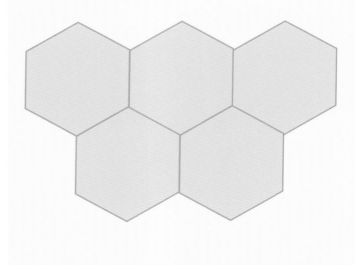

➡️ Symmetry

We will look at which shapes have symmetry.

Symmetry is when a line drawn through the shape can divide it so that it looks the same on both sides.
Sometimes this is called a mirror line.

Square

Does a square have a line of symmetry?

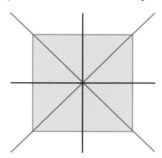

A square can have a line of symmetry across the diagonals from corner to corner.
It can also have a line of symmetry through the centre either horizontally or vertically.

They are on the lines where we would fold the square in half.

Triangle

A regular triangle has a line of symmetry from any angle to the middle of the opposite side.
It has three lines of symmetry altogether.

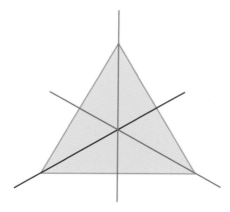

Not all triangles have lines of symmetry. You must be able to draw a line so that it is exactly the same on both sides.

Pentagon

A regular pentagon has a line of symmetry from any angle to the middle of the opposite side.
It has 5 lines of symmetry altogether.

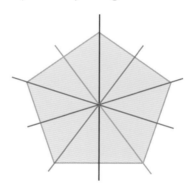

Hexagon

A regular hexagon has six lines of symmetry.
Hexagons have lines of symmetry from corner to corner or from the middles of opposite sides.

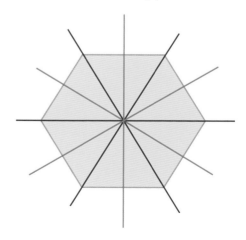

➡ Irregular shapes

What about shapes that are not regular?
Other shapes are not regular but can tessellate and have symmetry.

Rectangle

This is sometimes called an oblong.

It has two long sides opposite two shorter sides and four right-angled corners.

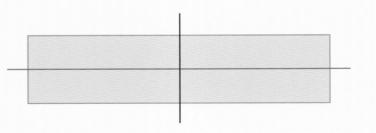

Rectangles have lines of symmetry through the centres of opposite sides.
Rectangles can tessellate. Think of these examples you see every day.

- Cereal Boxes
- Fence Panels

Triangle

Lots of triangles are not regular.
They have three sides but they are not all equal in length.

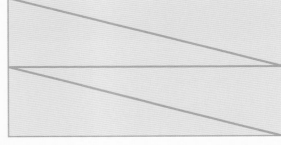

They can still tessellate.

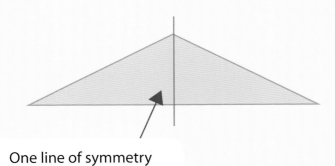

One line of symmetry

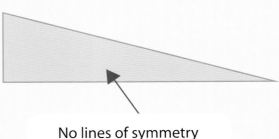

No lines of symmetry

They do not always have lines of symmetry.

Other shapes

Lots of other irregular shapes can tessellate and some also have lines of symmetry.
They can be used to make patterns, for example, in floor, wall and roof tiles.

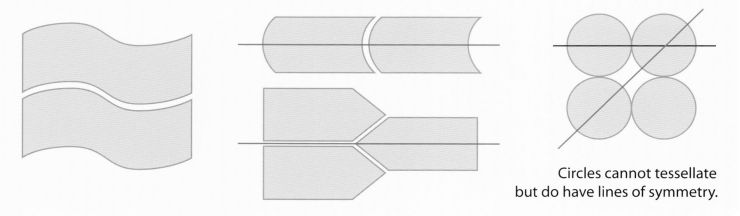

Circles cannot tessellate
but do have lines of symmetry.

Perimeters and areas

Lots of learners find the difference between **Perimeter** and **Area** quite confusing so let's have a look at what they are.

Why do I need to know this?
To measure the spaces around us when buying furniture and items for our home.
To work out how much paint or paper we need to decorate a room.
To know how far a distance is around something.
To compare two different sizes.

 ## Perimeter

The perimeter is the distance around the outside of a closed shape.
The word comes from the Greek **peri** meaning '**around**' and **meter** meaning '**to measure**'.

If you wanted to find the perimeter of a rectangle you need to know the lengths of all the sides and you **add** them up to find the total distance.

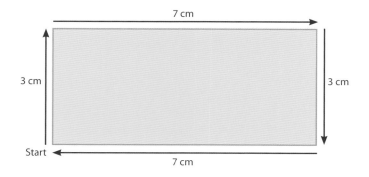

If you are not confident working out perimeters, take care to make sure you have included all the lengths. You could draw lines along each length to help you and write them down as you go.
Make sure all the lengths are in the same units, e.g. all mm, or all cm, or all m.

3 cm + 7 cm + 3 cm + 7 cm = 20 cm
The perimeter is 20 cm.

Irregular shapes can be more complicated, but the perimeter is still worked out in the same way. It is always a total of all the sides around the shape.

This is the plan of a room

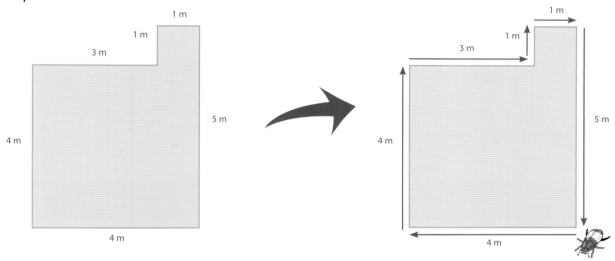

A beetle walks around the perimeter of the room to get some exercise; he wants to know how far he has walked.

4 + 4 + 3 + 1 + 1 + 5 = 18 m

The beetle has walked 18 m.

➡ Area

Area is the amount of space or number of square units inside a perimeter.

This shape is 5 squares x 6 squares.

The area is the number of squares inside.
We find this out by **multiplying** the length or height by the width of the rectangle or square.

5 x 6 = 30 squares

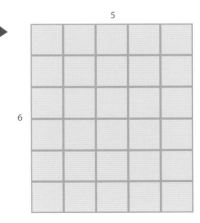

When you write the answer to an area calculation you always use a '**squared**' symbol to show that you have multiplied two numbers together to get the answer.

...Maths likes symbols. They save us writing things out in full.

This garden is 7 metres x 4 metres.

The area is 7 x 4 = 28 square metres.

Square metres is a nuisance to write in full every time so we use an m for the metres and a raised 2 to show the square (^{2}).

Like this: 28 m^2

Don't forget the units!

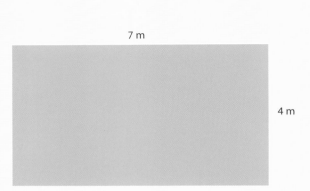

Take Care!
When you are finding an **Area** you **Always Multiply.**
Before you multiply the lengths make sure they are in the same units, e.g. all mm, or all cm, or all m.

There is more information about this in the section on Measuring things and Converting units.

Other shapes

If we are measuring the beetle's room we need to draw in a line to make two shapes and we can easily work out the area of each one.

There are two ways to put a dividing line into this shape; it doesn't matter which one we use.

Sometimes shapes need **dividing up** *to find the* **area**

The **FIRST** way

The first dividing line makes two shapes: the first is 4 m x 4 m and the second is 1 m x 1 m.

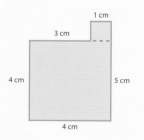

$$\begin{array}{r} 4 \\ \times \quad 4 \\ \hline 1\,6 \end{array} \qquad \begin{array}{r} 1 \\ \times \quad 1 \\ \hline 1 \end{array}$$

16 + 1 = 17 ^{m2}

The **SECOND** way

The second dividing line makes two shapes: the first is 5 m x 1 m and the second is 4 m x 3 m.

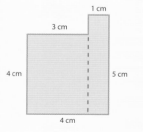

$$\begin{array}{r} 5 \\ \times \quad 1 \\ \hline 5 \end{array} \qquad \begin{array}{r} 4 \\ \times \quad 3 \\ \hline 1\,2 \end{array}$$

5 + 12 = 17 ^{m2}

Both ways will give you the same answer!

Volume

Why do I need to know this?
Workplaces use volume to find out how many people can work in the space. You can work out how much concrete or soil is needed for laying a drive or path. Understanding volume helps you with the units in everyday use, on packaging, for example.

When we work them out we have to measure the length, the width and the height or depth.
We multiply **all three measurements** to find the volume.

The answer is shown as a **cubed** unit.

What does that mean?

Remember areas? They had a squared unit, so when we used metres (m) the answer was in square metres (m^2).
We showed the 'square' by writing a small ^{2} in the answer.
When we work out volume we write a small ^{3} in the answer.

This is shorthand for **cubed**.

Let's look at a box to find out why we need to multiply 3 numbers...

This box is filled with 1 cm blocks.

The green blocks show one complete section. No more blocks can be fitted in here, so we have to start a new section behind it.

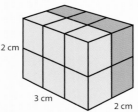

2 cm

3 cm   2 cm

We can think of the box as a series of 'slices'. When we work out volume we work out the area of the first 'slice'.

The green slice has an area of 2 cm x 3 cm
$2 \times 3 = 6$ cm^2.

We multiply the area by the number or depth of 'slices' to find the volume.

6 cm x 2 cm = 12 cm³.

Remember!

Area is 2 numbers multiplied together and has a small ^{2} in the answer (e.g. m^2).
Volume is 3 numbers multiplied together and has a small ^{3} in the answer (e.g. m^3).

Here's another example...

You have a new plant tub, which is 2 m by 0.3 m by 0.3 m.
What is the volume of soil you will need to fill it?

The sum is 2 x 0.3 x 0.3 = **0.12 m³**.
The answer sounds very small,
but remember 1 m³ is a volume 1m x 1m x 1m.

Take Care!
Make sure all three numbers are in the same units (mm, cm, m). You must convert them before starting the sum.

One more example...

A sandpit needs refilling after being cleaned.
What is the volume of sand needed to fill it?

Take Care!
We can't use *mixed units.* We must change them to be the same. We can use metres or centimetres, and we decide which is the easiest by looking at the question.

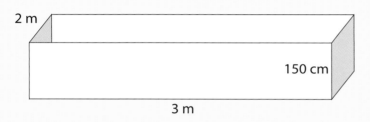

2 m

150 cm

3 m

We work out the area of one side first.
3 m x 150 cm

Alert! We have metres and centimetres in this sum.

This sum already has two values using metres and the numbers are small which makes them easier to calculate with so we will convert from centimetres to metres.

We need to convert 150 cm to metres.

100 cm = 1 metre   so   150 cm = 1.5 m.

Now we can do the sum with the area of one side first.
3 m x 1.5 m = 4.5 m²

Now multiply by the depth   4.5 x 2 = 9 m³.

The volume of sand needed is 9 m³.

We can cross out the 150 cm and write in 1.5 m so we don't forget.

Mathematicians write things down; they don't want to forget anything!

Using scale

What is scale?
We use scale to make things easier to use.
A plan of a room can't be drawn full-size; it would be as big as the actual room!
If we decide on a scale we can draw the room much smaller but still in the same proportions.

Why do I need to know this?
Scale drawings are used for making plans of rooms and gardens.
Maps are drawn to scale; you can calculate approximate distances from a map.
Scales are used on graphs and charts.

For example, an office is 4 m x 3 m.

If we draw 10 cm for every metre of the full size, the drawing will be 40 cm x 30 cm.

10 cm x 4 = 40 cm
10 cm x 3 = 30 cm   The **scale is 10 cm = 1 m.**

This is a good size for a large room plan, but if we wanted to draw the room on a smaller sheet of paper it still would not fit and we would need to use a smaller **scale**.

Here is a map...

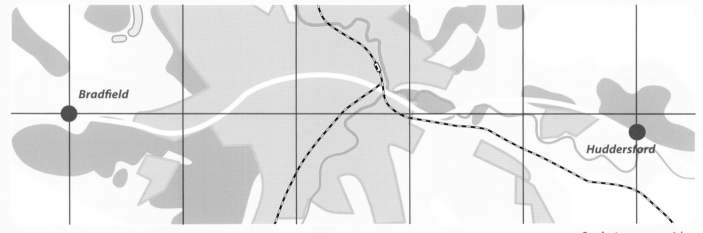

Scale *1 square = 1 km*

Use the scale to work out how many km it is from Bradfield to Huddersford

The scale is 1 square for every 1 km

We can count the squares along the road between the two places.
There are approximately 5 squares between Bradfield and Huddersford.

5 x 1 = 5 km

From the scale above we know that **Bradfield is approximately 5 km from Huddersford.**

Functional Skills **MATHEMATICS**

Now try this question...

Mary wants to have a new kitchen fitted.
Her kitchen is 4 m x 3 m.
She wants to draw her plans onto squared graph paper.
The squares on the paper are 1 cm x 1 cm.

What would be a good scale to use for her drawing?

We need the drawing to be big enough to use so
1 cm to 1 m would be much too small.

We could use 4 squares on the paper for every metre of the
full size. This would make each 1 cm square equal to ¼ metre
and make it easier for Mary to draw her plan.

Working out the scale
4 cm : 1 m
1 cm : 0.25 m
0.25 m = 25 cm

Scale is 1:25

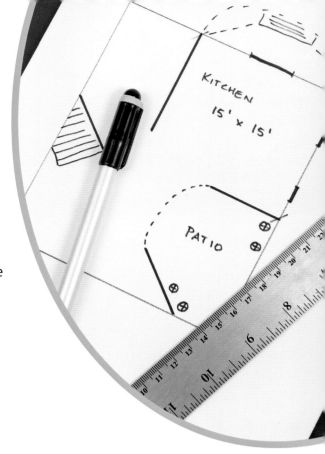

Next question...

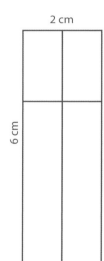

2 cm

6 cm

This window has been drawn using a scale of 2 cm to every 1 m.

How big is the actual window?

Every 2 cm is equal to 1 m of real size.
We need to work out how many lots of 2 cm we can divide into the scaled measurements.

2 cm ÷ 2 cm = 1
6 cm ÷ 2 cm = 3

The window is 1 m x 3 m.

Functional Skills **MATHEMATICS**

Graphs, tables, charts, and other sources of information

→ Reading and understanding information

Let's look at what we can find out from charts, graphs and tables.

We use different methods, but they are all ways of showing information.
Some of the methods we can use are pie charts, bar charts, line graphs, tables, pictograms, tally charts, drawings and lists.

We have different ways of showing information because some methods work better for some types of information.

Here are some simple ways which are used in everyday life to show information.

Why do I need to know this?
We often use tables, graphs and diagrams to show and read information.

Price lists, catalogues and temperature charts are just a few of the things we need to know how to use in everyday life.
Assembly drawings may be used in furniture packs.

You will need to know this to help you pass a Functional Skills test.
You may need to know this for work when showing results or sales for example.
You may want to collect information yourself to improve your garden crops or save money on bills for example.

A price list

Hair Cutting Price List

Dry cut	£18.00
Cut and style	£27.50
Cut, style and treatment	£37.00
Cut and colour	£46.50

This is a good way of showing prices for a hairdresser's.
We can easily see the different prices and choose the one we want to use.

A diagram

This is a drawing showing how to assemble a shelving unit.
We can see how the pieces fit together without having to read any words.

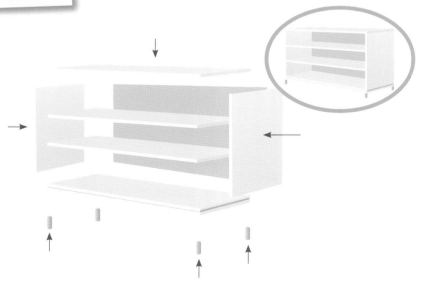

A plan drawing

This plan is showing a drawing of a bedroom.
We can easily see the layout of the room, but we need labels to be sure about what all the shapes are.

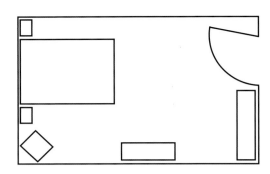

A pictogram

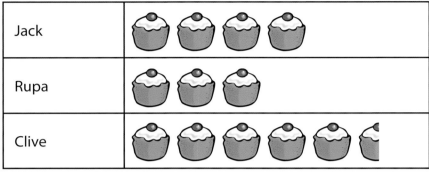

Jack	
Rupa	
Clive	

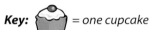
Key: = one cupcake

Take Care!
One pictogram symbol doesn't always have to mean one object. Some pictograms use one symbol to mean a quantity of objects.

For example:
If you were counting red cars, one pictogram car could represent 5 cars or 10 cars.

This is a good way of showing simple information.
The pictogram shows how many cupcakes three friends have eaten in the previous week.
Each cupcake represents one cupcake that has been eaten; half a cupcake shows that half a cupcake was eaten.
A pictogram always needs a key to show what the symbols mean.
It is easy to see how many cakes the friends have eaten using a pictogram.

A tally chart

Another good way of showing simple information is with a tally chart.
Sometimes this is called using 5-bar gates. That is because the tally looks like a 5-bar gate.

Tally charts count up in 5s like this; the last line drawn crosses through the other four.

| One | Two | Three | Four | Five |

Blue cars	۱۱۱۱ ۱۱۱۱ ۱۱۱۱ ۱۱
Red cars	۱۱۱۱ ۱۱۱۱ ۱۱۱۱ ۱
Green cars	۱۱۱۱ ۱۱۱۱ ۱۱۱
Silver cars	۱۱۱۱ ۱۱۱۱ ۱۱
Black cars	۱۱۱۱ ۱۱۱۱ ۱۱۱۱ ۱۱۱۱

Here is a tally chart of cars seen on a road one morning.
It shows which colours are the most popular.

We can count up the 'gates' in fives and add on any remaining lines.
There were 17 blue cars.

Functional Skills **MATHEMATICS**

Mileage Chart

A mileage chart shows us information on distances between places to help us plan a journey.
It uses a grid or table layout.

We need to find the information we need
by reading across the grid.

**Mary has to drive from her home in Leeds
to her friend in Doncaster.
How many miles will she travel there and back?**

The way to look up the miles is to draw a line across
and down from the town names you are using.

You can see that where the lines meet it shows the
distance between Leeds and Doncaster is 35 miles.

To work out the return trip 35 x 2 = **70 miles.**

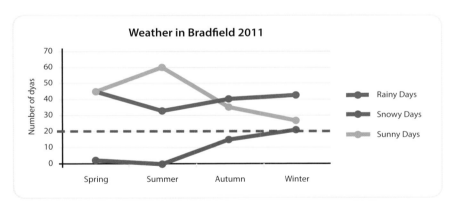

Distances shown in miles

Line Graph

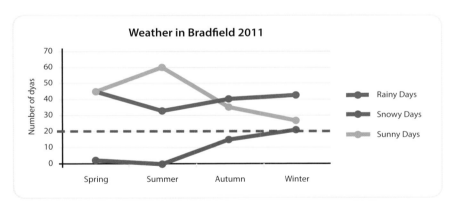

A line graph can be used to compare
information and is better for more
complex information.

In this example we can compare weather
at different times of the year.

A line graph is drawn by plotting the
points and joining them up with a line.

To read a value from the graph we need to use a ruler or guide to read across from the marker to the scale at
the side. This is shown by a red dashed line.
We can see there were 20 days of snow in the winter months.
We can see how the rainy days increase in the winter and the sunny days decrease.

Line graphs can show us information
about one thing as well.

We can easily see how the temperature
increased at the weekend.

We can see that Wednesday was the
coldest day and Saturday the warmest.

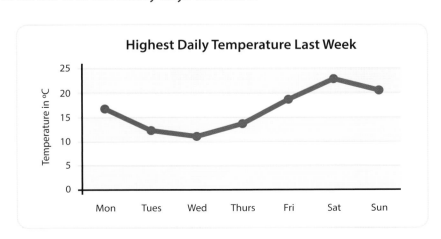

Bar Chart

A bar chart is good for comparing results. It is good for more complicated information and it is used for showing information about more than one thing.

This bar chart shows information about favourite foods. It shows the number of people who like different foods.

We can use a ruler or guide to follow a line from the top of the bar to the scale at the side.
Then we can read off the scale to see how many people like the different foods.

The red line shows that 15 people like chocolate. We can also see that apples were the least favourite food.

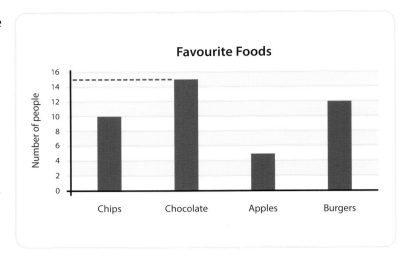

Pie Chart

A pie chart is a good visual method for showing information.
It is used to compare information.

There can be values on a pie chart showing the percentage value or the actual numbers used, but a lot of information can be understood just from comparing the sections.

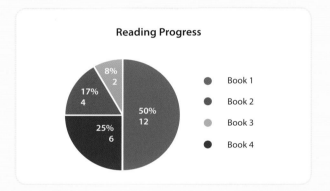

In this pie chart we can compare children's reading.
Most children are on the easiest book, book 1; the fewest children are on the hardest book, book 3.

It is easy to see the proportions in a pie chart. For example we can see that about half the children are on the first book and about a quarter of them are on book 4 just by looking at the size of the coloured sections.

Remember! →

Important things about extracting information.
Use a guide or ruler to **read the scale accurately**.
See if there are two or more pieces of *information* you can compare.

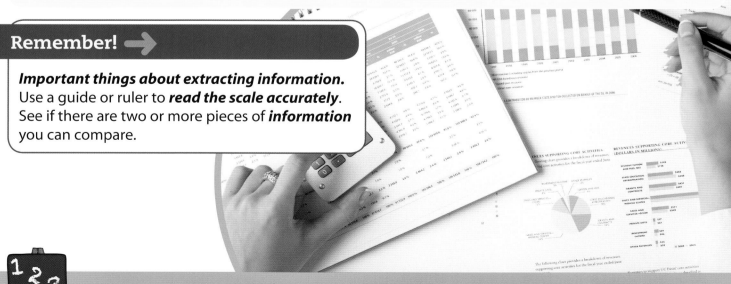

Functional Skills **MATHEMATICS**

➡ Collecting information

In a Functional Skills test we may be given the information, usually called **data**.
We may have to collect some data or work it out from the information given in the test.

The data we are given may be in a tally chart, pictogram or table for example.
We may have to draw our own tally chart, pictogram or table using information given to us in the test.

Another method for collecting information or data can be in a questionnaire or survey.
If collecting data is part of your test, there will be marks awarded for collecting it in an appropriate way.

The two simplest ways of collecting data are in a **tally chart** or in a **questionnaire**.

Tally chart

A tally chart uses the five-bar-gate symbol and counts up in 5s. The last line drawn crosses through the other four to show the 'gate' is a complete 5.

| One | Two | Three | Four | Five |

They are quick to use and make it easy to count up any results.

Questionnaire

A questionnaire can be written to ask only the questions we are really interested in having information about.

For example, if we wanted to find out about how many people watched a specific music channel we could ask about that TV channel and not just about TV in general.

The important thing to remember with a questionnaire is to keep questions very simple and easy to answer.
Try to think about what information you really want to collect.

➡ Showing information

Once we have collected our data we can decide how to show it. We usually say **represent** it.
We will look at four ways of showing or representing data.

Pictogram

In the pictogram we looked at before we could see how many cupcakes three friends had eaten.

When you draw a pictogram be careful to draw the symbols or pictures you use carefully so that is shows your data accurately.

It is easy to read but can be time-consuming to draw if there is a lot of data to show.

Key:  = one cupcake

Jack	🧁🧁🧁🧁
Rupa	🧁🧁🧁
Clive	🧁🧁🧁🧁🧁🧁

Remember! ➡

One symbol can mean more than one item being counted.

Table

A table can be a simple grid or list.
It needs to clearly show the information.
Columns or rows need titles so we can understand what the numbers mean.

Here is an example of using a table...

Jo is planning a meal for some friends.
The food needs to be ready for 7 p.m.
She is making chicken, roast potatoes and mixed vegetables.
Chicken takes 2 hours, the roast potatoes take 1 hour and the vegetables take half an hour.

The table needs to be laid before the food has finished cooking.

We will write a plan to make sure everything is ready on time.

This plan is written as a table.
It is easy to see what is happening at each time.
The times are written in order.
The table has labels at the top of the columns.
It also has a title underneath it.

Time	Activity
5 p.m.	Start cooking chicken
5.15 p.m.	Lay table
6 p.m.	Start roasting potatoes
6.30 p.m.	Start cooking vegetables
7 p.m.	Meal is ready

Plan to help prepare the meal on time.

Line Graph

Sales Person	Weekly Sales of Socks in January			
Jane	11	20	18	27
Joan	15	17	14	15
Jerry	27	13	15	10
	Week 1	Week 2	Week 3	Week 4

A sock company wants to compare the performance of three salespeople.
They have collected the following information.

We can use graph paper to show this data more clearly.

Here we can see how the data in the table has been used to draw a line graph to compare the sales people's results.

We can easily see with a line graph that Jane's sales have gone up while Jerry's have gone down.

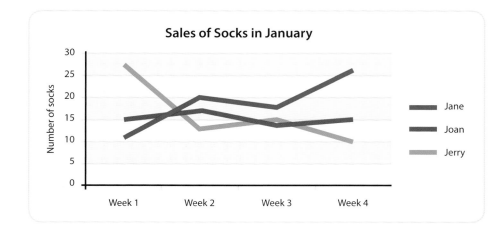

A graph has some important things on it

- **A title**
- **Axes titles**
    We call the line going from left to right the **x-axis**
    (this one shows the weeks).
    We call the line going up and down the side the **y-axis**
    (this one shows the **scale** for the numbers of socks).
- **A legend**
    This shows us what each coloured line represents
    (here it is the name of the salesperson).
- **A scale**
    The scale must be even
    (here it shows the number of socks starting at zero and increasing in units of 5).
- **Accurate plotting**
    The data must be plotted accurately to show the information correctly.

Bar Chart

There is a quiz night in the local community centre.
6 teams have competed in 5 rounds of questions.
The organiser has recorded the results of the teams in a table.

Team Name	Total
Wow Factor	90
The Green Wellies	94
The Rebels	76
Fast and Furious	49
Beauty and Beast	80
Great Guessers	44

He wants to compare the teams' total scores.
We can use graph paper to show the total scores for the teams.

Here is a graph showing the total scores.

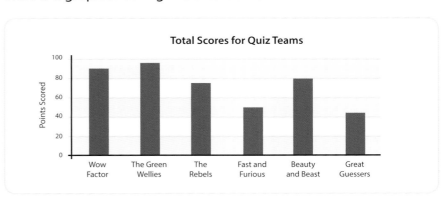

The bar chart shows how well the teams did and lets us compare them easily.

When we draw a bar chart we need to decide on the scale we will use for the y-axis.
Although on most graphs the y-axis starts at zero, it can start at any value.
For example, if there were no values to show below 100 we could start the y-axis at 100.
The scale on the y-axis must always be consistent.

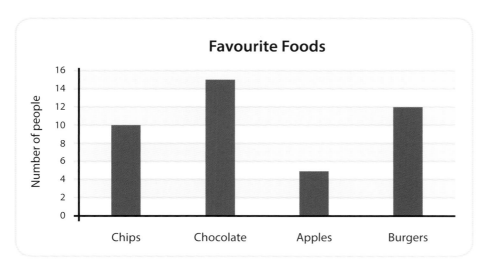

The scale lines on this chart are drawn at intervals of every 2 people. This is easy to read.

Look what happens if we change the scale to one line for every person:

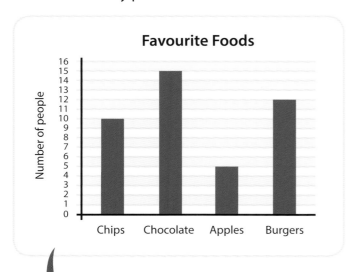

Remember! →

A chart has some important things on it
- *A title*
- *Axes titles*
- *A scale* needs to be even, usually starting at zero. A scale always increases in regular units.
- *Accurate plotting* is essential to show the information correctly.

It has to get taller to space the lines out or it is harder to see the numbers on the scale.

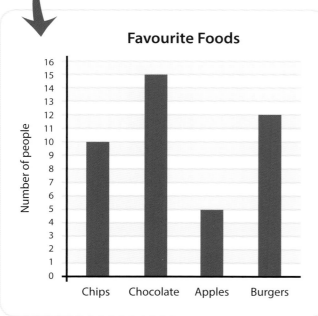

You can choose your own scale when you draw a chart or graph, but

...it must be easy to read.

Take Care!
It is easy to lose marks when you are representing data.

Choose an *appropriate method* to represent the data.
Use an *appropriate scale*.
The scale must be *consistent*.
Draw your graph, chart or table *accurately*.
Take care to use the *correct* numbers.
Draw your information *neatly and clearly*.
Write times or events in the *right order*.

Functional Skills **MATHEMATICS**

Mean and range

➡ Mean

The 'mean' is also called the 'average'. It is used very often in newspapers, reports, television programmes and other sources of information.

So how do we work out the mean?

To work out the mean we add up all the item values and divide by the number of items we have. Here is an example to explain it better.

Five people each have a pile of sweets. Here are the different numbers of sweets they have in their piles.

| 10 | 12 | 9 | 11 | 13 |

To work out the mean number of sweets per person we add the piles up.

$$10 + 12 + 9 + 11 + 13 = 55$$

Now we divide the total by the number of piles. The mean number of sweets each person has is 11.

$$55 \div 5 = 11$$

We have shared the sweets equally between the five people.

By adding the piles up and dividing them by the number of piles we had, we have spread out the piles equally.

Everyone has the same mean number of 11. The **mean** value is the **shared** value.

Take Care!
The **mean value** does not tell us the **actual value**.

In our example only one person actually has 11 sweets.

Here is another example, so we can look at why the mean can sometimes confuse us!

Seven students in a room want to know what their mean age is. Their ages are:

 21   **20**   **22**   **23**   **21**   **20**   **20**

To work out the mean we add up all the ages.

$$21 + 20 + 22 + 23 + 21 + 20 + 20 = 147$$

Now we divide the total 147 by the number of ages; there are seven of them.

The mean age is 21.

Look at the ages. Only 2 students are actually 21 but... the other ages are close to 21.
So when we say the mean age of the students is 21 it gives us a fairly accurate idea of how old the students actually are.

Distorted Averages

What happens when somebody in the room brings their 85 year old grand-mother with them?

Now the ages we have to add up are
$21 + 20 + 22 + 23 + 21 + 20 + 20 + 85 = 234$

This time we must divide by 8 because there are now 8 people in the room
$232 \div 8 = 29$

The mean age of the people in the room is 29.

Does this tell us anything useful about the actual ages of the people in the room?

Not really because
- nobody is 29
- most people are actually 20 - 23
- one person is 85 which is nowhere near 29.

What if somebody brings their sister with them as well? She is only 2.

Now the ages we have to add up are
$21 + 20 + 22 + 23 + 21 + 20 + 20 + 85 + 2 = 232$

We have to divide by 9 because there are 9 ages this time
$234 \div 9 = 26$

The mean age this time is 26.

Now the mean value is a bit closer to the age of most people in the room.
7 people are between 20 and 23.

But it doesn't tell us anything about the little sister or Grand-mother. They are 2 and 85, nowhere near the mean age of 26.

This effect happens often in the mean or average figures we read about in the papers or on the news.

We often read about the mean weekly wage people earn. When the newspaper says the average weekly wage is £450 per week it might sound much more than we are earning ourselves.

But if the mean was worked out using one or two people who earn much more than most, a footballer or famous singer for example, the mean value will go up.

This makes it *very confusing* because the mean wage might be £450, but nearly everyone will actually earn more or less than £450.

When we use a mean value in everyday life we really need to know a bit more about how it was worked out to understand what we really mean!

Take Care!
The mean can give a misleading result when there are any values that are much higher or lower than the rest.

 Range

When we looked at the mean ages knowing the range would have helped us understand how useful the mean value was.

Range measures the spread of the data we are using

Look...

When Grand-mother and the little sister were in the room too we had these ages:

| 21 | 20 | 22 | 23 | 21 | 20 | 20 | 85 | 2 |

To work out the range we *find the largest value and take away the smallest value*.

85 - 2 = 83

The range is 83.

We still don't know exactly how old everyone actually is but we can see there is a big difference between the oldest and youngest person.

We know that not everyone is close to the mean value of 26.

Did you notice the range was 83 and not 2 to 85?

In everyday life we often describe the range of something using both the lowest and highest numbers.

For example we might say the range of prices for a mobile phone is from £100 to £300.
In maths the range is the *difference*.
We find the largest value and take the smallest value away.

£300 - £100 = £200

In maths the range for the phone prices is £200.

Mathematicians like to be different!

Remember! →

In Maths the range is a *single value*.

Probability

Probability is **how likely something is to happen**.

We often call it chance, or likelihood.

We say 'what is the chance that something will happen?'
We could say 'what is the probability that something will happen?'

Probability is written in fractions, percentages, decimals or on a probability scale.

" **Probability** is how likely something is to happen "

That sounds complicated but let's take a look and see...

If something is likely to happen, for example the sun shines in the summer, we say it has a **high probability** of happening.

We mean it is more likely to happen than not to happen.

Think about these events...

January will be the next month after December.

You will feel hungry today.

Some days in June will be hot.

It will snow in February.

We can see that some things can have a probability of 1 because they are certain to happen.
For example '***January will be the next month after December***'.

Some things are very likely to happen but are not certain to happen.
For example '***You will feel hungry today***' and '***Some days in June will be hot***'.

And some things are likely to happen but are not certain to happen.
For example '***It will snow in February***'.

If something is unlikely to happen, for example the sun shines every day for a month, we say it has a **low probability** of happening.

We mean it is more likely not to happen than to happen.

Think about these events...

You happen to meet an old friend on the train.	Some things are **unlikely** to happen but could happen. **You bump into an old friend on the train.**
The sun shines brightly every day of the summer.	Some things are **very unlikely** to happen but could happen. **The sun shines brightly every day of the summer.**
You win a big prize in a competition.	Some things are **unlikely** to happen but could happen. **You win a big prize in a competition.**
A dog has kittens.	Some things have a probability of 0 because they are **impossible.** **A dog has kittens.**

➡ Probability scale

We can write probability using a **probability scale.**
Zero is something that is impossible.
The number one is something that is certain to happen.

1	Certain to happen
¾	Very likely to happen (¾ is the same as 0.75 or 75%)
½	Even chance of happening (½ is the same as 0.5 or 50%)
¼	Not very likely to happen (¼ is the same as 0.25 or 25%)
0	Impossible

Look at the scale. You can see that because we use 1 to represent something which is certain to happen, the scale can show the probability, or chance, of something as a fraction, decimal or percentage.

For example
Something that might happen - you get a letter from an old friend.
It is not certain to happen.
It is not impossible.

We need to put it somewhere on the probability scale in-between 0 and 1.

If it is equally likely to happen as not to happen we would say it had an **even chance**.

We can mark that halfway along the scale.
Halfway between 0 and 1 is ½.

If you can't quite remember how we get from fractions to decimals or percentages have another look in the sections explaining this in more detail to remind yourself.

We can say the probability of getting a letter from an old friend is ½.
We can also write ½ as 0.5 or 50%.

Who needs to know about probablity and chance?

Here is someone who uses it everyday....

An insurance company uses probability to work out how likely it is that an accident or event will happen. They work out how much to charge their customers so that they don't lose all their money in claims.

Think about this....

Is health insurance going to be more expensive for a relaxing holiday in the sun or for a skiing trip in the mountains?

You are more likely to have an accident skiing so the insurance company will charge more for insuring a holiday like that than for someone who will be relaxing by the swimming pool every day.

They use the same idea for car insurance.
An insurance company will look at the likelihood or chance that someone will have an accident.
They use the information on accidents that happened last year to help them work it out.
Someone who is more likely to have an accident will be asked to pay more for their car insurance than someone who is more likely to be a safer driver.

Possible outcomes

If someone has a baby what is the chance it will be a girl?

Mmm... a baby could be a boy or a girl.

There are **2 possible outcomes**.

There is a **one in two chance** (½) of the baby being a girl.

If we throw a die, what are the chances it will be an odd number?

There are 6 possible outcomes from throwing a die, 1, 2, 3, 4, 5 or 6.

There are **3 possible outcomes** for throwing an odd number, 1, 3 or 5.

We can throw an odd number in three different ways.

(3/6 this is the same as ½).

Are we more likely to throw an odd number than a six with one die?

The chance of throwing an odd number is 3/6 or ½.
The chance of throwing a 6 is one in six (1/6).
There are 6 possible outcomes from throwing the die, 1, 2, 3, 4, 5 or 6.
There is only one number 6.
½ is more likely than 1/6.

The probability is that we might be successful once in every two throws of the die instead of only once in every six throws of the die.

We can see that we work out the chance or probability of something happening by dividing the number of ways something can happen by the possible outcomes.

Remember! →

To work out the probability or chance divide the number of ways something can happen by the possible outcomes.

For example

The baby is a girl.

There are 2 ways of having a baby, a boy or a girl.

There is only 1 possible outcome for having a girl.

We can say there is a 1 in 2 chance of having a girl.

The die is an odd number.

There are 6 ways of throwing a die, 1, 2, 3, 4, 5 or 6.

There are 3 possible outcomes, 1, 3 or 5.

We can say there is a 3 in 6 chance of throwing an odd number.

3 in 6 is the same as 1 in 2 so we can also say there is a 1 in 2 chance of throwing an odd number.

The die is a 6.

There are 6 ways of throwing the die, 1, 2, 3, 4, 5 or 6.

There is 1 possible outcome for throwing a 6.

We can say there is a 1 in 6 chance of throwing a 6.

Here is a new one

If we toss a coin what is the chance it will land heads up?

There are two ways of tossing the coin, heads or tails.
There is one possible outcome.
We can say there is a 1 in 2 chance of throwing a head.
The probability is that we will throw a head once in every two throws of the die.

Take Care!
The probability, likelihood or chance does not mean it will actually always turn out to be true every time. It is a chance, not a certainty.

Remember we can write all these as fractions, decimals or percentage values

One in two is the same as
½ or 0.5 or 50%

1 in 6 is the same as
1/6 or 0.16 or 16%

They all mean the same thing; they are just written in different ways

That's Maths Magic!

List of useful words

Appropriate	a value or method that is suitable
Approximate check	checking a calculation by using whole numbers close to the values in the sum
Axis or axes	the horizontal and vertical scale lines on a graph or chart
Chunking	a method for dividing numbers
Comparing	looking at what is different or the same about two or more things or numbers
Denominator	the bottom number in a fraction
Distorted average	a mean value that is changed by having a higher or lower value than the rest of the data
Equivalent	having the same value as another number or fraction
Estimating	working out a value based on whole numbers close to the ones in the sum
Five-bar gate	another name for tally lines
Formula	a number 'recipe' to follow which works something out
Fraction wall	a chart or table comparing different fractions of 1
Lattice method	a method for multiplying numbers
Method	this is the way you work something out
Mirror line	another name for a line of symmetry
Multiples	numbers that come from counting up by adding on the same number each time
Number bonds	groups or pairs of numbers that together add up usually to 10 or 100
Numerator	the top number in a fraction
Order	to put numbers into position according to their size
Parallel	two lines that run straight, but never get any closer or further away from each other
Partitioning	a method of adding and subtracting that works out each place value separately
Perimeter	the distance around the outside of a shape
Place value	this is the position of any digit in a number
Plot	to mark onto a graph the position of the points
Probability scale	a range from 0 to 1 showing the likelihood of something happening

Functional Skills **MATHEMATICS**

List of useful words

Recurring numbers	decimal places which cannot be divided by a whole number
Rounding	simplifying a number to a nearest value or specific number of decimal places
Simplifying	putting numbers into their basic form or lowest division
Square numbers	numbers that come from two smaller numbers multiplied by themselves
Symmetry	when the shapes either side of a centre line are identical
Tally lines	a system of counting in fives where 4 small lines are crossed through by a fifth line
Tessellate	when a repeated shape pattern can fit together with no gaps

Metric tables

WEIGHT

1000 grams (g)	1 kilogram
1000 Kilograms (kg)	1 metric ton

TEMPERATURE

100° Centigrade (°C)	Boiling point
0°C	Freezing point

LENGTH AND DISTANCE

10 millimetres (mm)	1 centimetre (cm)
100 cm	1 metre (m)
1000 mm	1 m
1000 m	1 kilometre (km)

TIME

60 seconds	1 minute
60 minutes	1 hour
24 hours	1 day
7 days	1 week
52 weeks	1 year

VOLUME

100 centilitres (cl)	1 litre (l)
1000 cm^3	1 l
1000 l	1 m^3

Functional Skills **MATHEMATICS**

Notes